SRA Language Roundup

GREEN BOOK

Level 3

Dr. Betty Jane Wagner

SRA/McGraw-Hill

Columbus, Ohio

Author

Betty Jane Wagner

Professor
Reading and Language Department
National-Louis University
Evanston, IL

Cover Photo
Grades 2, 3, 4, 6, Aaron Haupt; Grade 5, John Gillmoure/The Stock Market

Illustration
Steve McInturff

SRA/McGraw-Hill

*A Division of The **McGraw·Hill** Companies*

Copyright © 1997 SRA/McGraw-Hill.
All rights reserved. Except as permitted under the United States
Copyright Act, no part of this publication may be reproduced or
distributed in any form or by any means, or stored in a database
or retrieval system, without prior written permission from the
publisher, unless otherwise indicated.

Send all inquiries to:
SRA/McGraw-Hill
4400 Easton Commons
Columbus, OH 43219

Printed in the United States of America

ISBN 0-02-687822-4

14 15 16 17 HES 13 12 11 10

Table of Contents

Mechanics ....

Usage ....

Special Problems

Grammar ....

Parts of Speech

Sentences

1 Capitalization: Sentences, People, and Pets

At the beginning of a sentence, be sure to capitalize. With proper names, it is also wise.

.... Did You Know? ....

The first word in a sentence is capitalized.

> **B**asketball is fun to play.
> **W**here is my basketball?

The word *I* is capitalized.

> Do you think **I** can make a basket from here?

The names of people and pets are capitalized.

> **M**onica **W**ilson is the coach of our basketball team.
> **C**arlos is the best player on our team.
> We met **P**atty and **L**isa at the game.
> My cat, **B**oots, likes to play with a ball of yarn.

Show What You Know

Read the sentences below. From each pair of words in parentheses, choose the correct word, and circle it.

(Basketball, basketball) is a fast and exciting sport. In 1891 (james
   1
naismith, James Naismith) invented the game. Ted and (i, I) practice our jump
   2   3
shots after school. My dog, (Tipper, tipper), watches us shoot baskets in the
                                      4
backyard. (the, The) Chicago Bulls is a championship team. (michael jordan,
          5   6
Michael Jordan) is my favorite player in the NBA.

Score: _____   Total Possible: 6

Proofread

The paragraph below has six mistakes in capitalization. Draw three lines under each letter that should be capitalized.

Example: today i am nine years old.

Eight friends came to my birthday party. My brothers, josh and mike, and I planned the party. first we split up into teams and played basketball. Maria made the winning shot for our team. Then we drank gallons of water to cool off. mom knew just what i would want next. she had a big chocolate cake waiting on the kitchen table!

Practice

Write two sentences about what is happening in the picture. Give names to the people and pets.

1._____

_____

2._____

_____

Tips for Your Own Writing: Proofreading ....

Choose a piece of your own writing. Look at the first word of every sentence and all the names of people and pets. Did you capitalize their first letter?

Now you know how to get your reader's attention: Use capital letters!

2 Capitalization: Places

From Atlantic to Pacific, capitalizing place-names is terrific.

.... **Did You Know?**.......................

The major words in geographical names are capitalized.

Chicago	Arizona	Italy
Ohio River	Mount Rushmore	Pacific Ocean
Lake Huron	Asia	

We flew directly from Lyon, France, to Manchester, England.

The Rio Grande flows from the San Juan Mountains of Colorado to the Gulf of Mexico.

The names of roads, places, and buildings are capitalized.

Fairmont Avenue	Herald Square
Washington Monument	White House

The Sears Tower is taller than the Empire State Building.

Columbia Hospital is on Central Avenue.

. . . .

Show What You Know

Write the two words in each sentence that should be capitalized.

1. We're planning to take a trip throughout north america.

_____

2. My mom works at broadview hospital.

_____

3. My older brother wants to hike the grand canyon.

_____

Score: _____   Total Possible: 3

Proofread

The paragraph below has ten mistakes in capitalization. Draw three lines under each letter that should be capitalized. Draw a line through each letter that should not be capitalized.

Example: Name a famous Waterfall in New york.

Niagara Falls is one of the most beautiful sights in north america. It is on the niagara river about halfway between Lake Ontario and lake erie. The Horseshoe falls on the Canadian side of the River is 161 feet high. The american Falls is 167 feet high and is in the state of New York. Colored lights brighten the Falls at night.

Practice

Write a paragraph describing something you would like to see on a trip anywhere in the world. Use at least four place-names.

_____

_____

_____

Tips for Your Own Writing: Proofreading ....

The next time you address an envelope, check to make sure that you have capitalized all place-names.

Capital means "important." Do you know that Washington, D.C., is the capital of the United States?

3 Capitalization: People's Titles

Aunt Sarah and Mr. Lu begin their names and titles with capitals, too.

.... Did You Know? ....

Names showing how you are related to someone are capitalized only if they are used in place of or as part of the relative's name.

Fishing is **G**randpa's favorite hobby.
Every summer, my **g**randpa takes us fishing.
Last year, my **m**om caught a huge fish.
This year, **M**om caught only a cold.

Titles of respect used with names of persons are capitalized.

Dr. Elizabeth Blackwell   **M**rs. Alvarez
President Clinton   **M**r. Peter Tepper

Our class wrote letters to **M**ayor Busby.
Our teacher, **M**s. Whitley, knows the mayor.

Show What You Know

Read each pair of sentences. Underline the sentence that has the correct capitalization.

1. My Uncle has the same name as an American symbol.
    His name is Uncle Sam.

2. *The Cat in the Hat* was written by dr. Seuss.
    He was not really a doctor.

3. In *The Wizard of Oz,* Dorothy called out, "auntie Em."
    At the same time, her aunt worried about her.

4. A main character in *Peter Pan* was Captain Hook.
    He was the mean Captain of a pirate ship.

Score: _____   Total Possible: 4

Proofread

The sentences below have seven mistakes in capitalization. Draw three lines under each letter that should be capitalized. Draw a line through each letter that should not be capitalized.

Example: His Aunt is my grandma Andrews.

Every year, Mom, Aunt Tilly, and grandpa Johnson plan a family picnic. Every year, something goes wrong. One year it rained. My Uncle said that he didn't know he was coming to a swimming party. uncle Theo always jokes like that. One year, I was stung by three bees. One year, everyone got sunburned.

But mom is ready this year. She called the Doctor to find out the best bee sting medicine. She asked the pharmacist about the best sunscreen. She even is taking umbrellas. My Aunt is helping, too. grandpa said, "Your mother and aunt will probably remember everything but the food!"

Practice

Write two sentences about a special family celebration. Use family names and titles whenever possible.

1._____

_____

2._____

Tips for Your Own Writing: Proofreading ....

The next time you write to a relative, make sure you have capitalized all titles of respect when they are used as names or as parts of names.

 You're doing a capital job with capital letters!

4 Capitalization: Dates and Holidays

"Yes, it's true," I say. "Capitalize days of the week, months, and each holiday!"

.... Did You Know? ....

The names of the days of the week and the months of the year are capitalized.

Monday	**W**ednesday	**S**aturday
April	**J**uly	**O**ctober

Mai goes to the library every **T**uesday afternoon.
The hottest days of the summer are often in **J**uly.

The names of holidays are capitalized.

Labor **D**ay	**T**hanksgiving	**P**residents' **D**ay

Flag **D**ay is celebrated on June 14.
I look forward to **C**olumbus **D**ay every year.

The names of the four seasons of the year are not capitalized.

spring	**s**ummer	**f**all	**w**inter

Show What You Know

Read the sentences below. If the underlined part contains an error in capitalization, circle the words that should be capitalized.

We honor Americans who gave their lives for our country on <u>Memorial day</u>[1]. Memorial Day is celebrated on the last <u>monday</u>[2] in <u>may</u>[3]. Some people call this holiday <u>decoration day</u>[4]. Flowers and flags are placed on the graves of military personnel in <u>spring</u>[5]. Many towns have parades on Memorial Day and <u>independence day</u>[6] to honor people who served our country.

Score: _____   Total Possible: 7

Proofread

The paragraph below has six mistakes in capitalization. Draw three lines under each letter that should be capitalized. Draw a line through each letter that should not be capitalized.

Example: My birthday is in the ~~F~~all on <u>o</u>ctober 9.

Groundhog day is an American tradition that supposedly predicts when Spring will arrive. According to legend, the groundhog comes out of its burrow on february 2. If the sun is shining, the groundhog sees its shadow. The groundhog will go back to its burrow, and there will be six more weeks of Winter. If it's cloudy, the groundhog doesn't see its shadow. The groundhog will stay outside, and Spring will arrive soon. An early spring means lots of blooming flowers in april.

Practice

Write two sentences about different holidays. Use a calendar to find out when each holiday occurs.

1. _____

   _____

2. _____

   _____

Tips for Your Own Writing: Proofreading . . . .

Choose a schedule you have written. Make sure you have capitalized the names of the months, days, and holidays. Remember, do not capitalize the names of the seasons.

 Said December to winter, "I get a cap, but you don't!"

5 Capitalization: Titles

Read out loud. Sing out strong. Capitalize titles, and you won't go wrong.

.... Did You Know?........................

The first word, last word, and other important words in titles are capitalized.

Book:	<u>W</u>ayside <u>S</u>chool <u>I</u>s <u>F</u>alling <u>D</u>own
Movie:	<u>F</u>ree <u>W</u>illy
Story:	"The Fox and the Crow"
Poem:	"Books to the Ceiling"
Song:	"The Star-Spangled Banner"

Show What You Know

Write each item. Use the rules you know to capitalize each title correctly.

1. "the ransom of red chief" _____

2. james and the giant peach _____

3. rebecca of sunnybrook farm _____

4. the wizard of oz _____

5. treasure island _____

6. home alone _____

7. "mary had a little lamb" _____

8. "over the rainbow" _____

Score: _____   **Total Possible: 8**

Proofread

The paragraph below has ten mistakes in capitalization. Draw three lines under each letter that should be capitalized.

Example: One of my favorite books is Annie and the old one.

Not another rainy Saturday—we just couldn't decide what to do! Lisa wanted to go to see the movie rookie of the year. Mark was happy to stay home and read the lion, the witch, and the wardrobe. No one wanted to sit around and recite "The Midnight Ride of Paul Revere." We ended up singing old camp songs like "the bear went over the mountain" and toasting marshmallows in the fireplace!

Practice

Make a list of your favorite songs, books, and movies. Make sure to capitalize the titles correctly. Then share the list with your classmates.

Lessons 11–16

_____

_____

_____

_____

_____

Tips for Your Own Writing: Proofreading ....

Choose a piece of your writing that has titles in it. Check to make sure all the important words have capital letters. If they do not, capitalize them.

In titles, it's a fact that all important words get capped.

6 Capitalization: Friendly Letters

Capital letters are the way to go when you open a letter or you close.

······················ **Did You Know?** ·····················

The first word in the greeting of a friendly letter is capitalized.

Dear Grandpa,   **H**i Leah,   **G**reetings friends,

The first word in the closing of a friendly letter is capitalized.

Best wishes,   **Y**our friend,

Thanks again,   **S**incerely yours,

···

Show What You Know

Read these greetings and closings for a friendly letter. Then write the correctly capitalized forms.

1. dear Mr. Clark,   _____

2. warmest regards,   _____

3. to my favorite cousin,   _____

4. yours truly,   _____

5. dearest Aunt Nell,   _____

6. until next time,   _____

7. very truly yours,   _____

8. with love,   _____

Score: _____   **Total Possible: 8**

Proofread

The friendly letter below has two mistakes in capitalization. Draw three lines under each letter that should be capitalized.

Example: I remembered to add "yours truly," to close my letter.

---

4 Pinewood Avenue
Alton, Pennsylvania   18106
June 27, 1996

dear Mr. Spinelli,

    Thank you for signing my copy of your book *Fourth-Grade Rats.* I do have a question. Next year, I will be in fourth grade. How do I go from being a third-grade angel to a fourth-grade rat? Can I be a fourth-grade good guy?

                            thank you,

                            Larry Cosgrove

Practice

On another piece of paper, write a friendly letter to a faraway friend inviting him or her to come for a visit.

Tips for Your Own Writing: Proofreading ....

Choose a letter that you have written. Check to make sure that you have correctly capitalized the greeting and closing.

Dear students,
        Without capital letters for the opening and closing, a letter would be wrong.

                            Your teacher,
                            Ms. Takes

7 Review: Capitalization

A. Draw three lines under the first letter of the nine words that should begin with capital letters.

last Tuesday, I got a new friend. he weighs about two pounds, has four legs, and has brown and white fur. I named him sport. He is a springer spaniel. Former President george bush had the same kind of dog. His dog's name was ranger. Ranger's mom, millie, lived in the White house. Mrs. bush wrote a book that saw life through Millie's eyes.

Score: _____   Total Possible: 9

B. The paragraph below has fourteen mistakes in capitalization. Draw three lines under each letter that should be capitalized. Draw a line through each letter that should not be capitalized.

The Panama Canal is a shortcut that ships can take between the atlantic Ocean and the pacific ocean. Before the canal was built, ships traveling from new york to san francisco had to sail around south america. In 1904, the united states paid panama $10 million for the rights to build the Canal. Workers from 97 countries from all over the World helped build the canal.

Score: _____   Total Possible: 14

C. Find and draw three lines under the first letter of the six words that should be capitalized.

I looked out into the audience and was glad to see mom, dad, and my brother, Tom. This was my first time playing in the school band, and my knees were shaking. I come from a long line of musicians—grandpa plays the banjo, uncle Bill plays the flute, and aunt Rita is a whiz on the piano. Our director, mr. Lanzt, held up his baton. I took a deep breath and blew into my tuba.

Score: _____   Total Possible: 6

D. The paragraph below has ten mistakes in capitalization. Draw three lines under each letter that should be capitalized. Draw a line through each letter that should not be capitalized.

December 26 is called boxing day in Britain, Australia, New zealand, and Canada. If december 26 falls on saturday or sunday, the official Celebration is always held on monday. On that day, people give money and gifts to Charities, the poor, and people in Service jobs.

Score: _____   Total Possible: 10

E. Draw three lines under the thirteen letters in the four titles that should be capitalized.

Our class earned $100 to purchase books for our classroom library. We voted to decide which books to buy. The two most popular were the polar express and mirette on the high wire. Nine students picked snow white and the seven dwarfs. Only I voted for talking like the rain.

Score: _____   Total Possible: 13

F. Find the two mistakes in capitalization in the friendly letter below. Draw three lines under each letter that should be capitalized.

456 Kingdom Lane
Happy, Storyland
May 24, 1997

dear Cinderella,

There I was happily eating cheese. Suddenly, I was turned into a horse. I had to pull a huge carriage. Please tell your fairy godmother not to make horses out of mice!

your friend,

Mr. Mouse

Score: _____   Total Possible: 2

REVIEW SCORE: _____   REVIEW TOTAL: 54

19

8 Punctuation: Periods

A period at the end of a sentence acts like a stop sign.

.... Did You Know? ....

A sentence that makes a statement ends with a period.

> Kevin let the dog out in the wet backyard.
> Blackie tracked mud all over the kitchen floor.

A sentence that makes a request ends with a period.

> Please mop the floor before Mom gets home.
> Leave the dog in the basement until he is dry.

An initial and an abbreviation of a title end with a period.

> Susan B. Anthony   Dr. Martin Luther King, Jr.
> Rev. Billy Graham   Ms. Jane Willis
> Mr. Lee Seung   Mrs. Margaret Watkins

Show What You Know

Read the sentences below. Add periods where they are needed. Circle them so that they are easier to see.

Our village held the dedication for a new park last week It is named the

Franklin D Roosevelt Park. Rev John Keats, Dr Suzanne Reed, and our mayor,

Ms Joan Montoya, each gave a speech. Mr Edward M Cameron cut the

opening ribbon. Capt Grooms directed the traffic. Mrs Mabel Keller and

members of her club served refreshments

Score: _____   **Total Possible: 10**

Proofread

This letter has five mistakes in punctuation. Add periods where they are needed. Circle them so that they are easier to see.

Example: Stop at the end.

---

50 Forest Lane
Fairy Tale Land
June 5, 1996

Dear Mr. and Mrs Elf,

    Thank you for making all the beautiful shoes My husband,

Mr Shoemaker, and I sold them. The little outfits in the boxes

are our way of thanking you I hope they fit.

        Thanks again,

        Mrs. Merry M Shoemaker

Practice

Write the names of your family members. Use abbreviations for their middle names and include their titles of respect, such as Mr. or Mrs.

_____

_____

_____

Tips for Your Own Writing: Proofreading ....

Choose a piece of your own writing. Make sure that each sentence that makes a statement and abbreviations of titles are followed by a period.

Yes, it is official. Use periods at the end of sentences, abbreviations, and initials.

9 Punctuation: Abbreviations

Make the days and months shorter. Abbreviate them and end with a period.

.... **Did You Know?** ....

An abbreviation for a day of the week ends with a period.

Monday—**Mon.**   Thursday—**Thurs.**   Saturday—**Sat.**
Tuesday—**Tues.**   Friday—**Fri.**   Sunday—**Sun.**
Wednesday—**Wed.**

An abbreviation for a month of the year ends with a period. There is no abbreviation for the months of May, June, and July.

January—**Jan.**   April—**Apr.**   October—**Oct.**
February—**Feb.**   August—**Aug.**   November—**Nov.**
March—**Mar.**   September—**Sept.**   December—**Dec.**

Show What You Know

Ramon's soccer schedule has mistakes in punctuation. Add periods where they are needed and circle them. If a day's name or a month's name is not abbreviated, but it could be, write the abbreviation on the line.

Wed July 14	Friday Aug 16	Tuesday Sept 3	Mon October 7	Sat Nov 9	Thurs Dec 19
____	____	____	____	____	____

Sunday Jan 21	Fri Feb 1	Monday Mar 16	Tues April 15	Saturday May 8	Thursday June 28
____	____	____	____	____	____

Score: _____   Total Possible: 21

Proofread

These entries from Mama Bear's journal have seven mistakes in punctuation. Use the proper proofreading marks to show where periods should be added to the entries.

Example: Feb 16. Today is Wed We are having a Valentine's party at school.

Mar 14. It snowed all day Sat and on Sun night. Papa Bear told Baby Bear to go back to sleep. He said all good baby bears sleep all the way through Nov, Dec, Jan., Feb., and Mar.

Apr. 7. Today is Sat, and Baby Bear woke up. She tried to shake Papa Bear awake. He just grunted and rolled over.

July 21. Last Thurs Papa Bear, Baby Bear, and I went for a walk. When we got home, we found a stranger in our house. Baby Bear cried because her chair was broken.

Practice

On another piece of paper, make a calendar for this month and show the days of the week. Use correct abbreviations. The calendar can be used to keep track of assignments and activities.

Tips for Your Own Writing: Proofreading ....

Choose a piece of your writing in which you have used abbreviations for months and days. Make sure you have added periods after each abbreviation.

Shortening the days and months is great, now that you know how to abbreviate.

10 Punctuation: Question Marks and Exclamation Points

Mark your questions with question marks. Point out your exclamations with exclamation points.

.... **Did You Know?**.........................

A sentence that asks a question ends with a question mark.

Have you seen my umbrella**?**

Do you like strawberries**?**

A sentence that expresses strong feelings ends with an exclamation point.

What a good job you did**!**

Help, I'm going to drop this package**!**

....

Show What You Know

Read the paragraph. Change two periods to question marks. Change one period to an exclamation point.

Do you know how the sandwich was invented. It was August 6, 1762, and John Montagu, the Earl of Sandwich, had been playing cards all day and night. Wow, was he hungry. He didn't want to leave the game. Do you know what he did. He told his servant to put some beef between two pieces of bread. Then he was able to eat while he continued to play cards. Ever since, any combination of filling and bread has been called a sandwich.

Score: _____   Total Possible: 3

Proofread

There are three mistakes in the punctuation in the report below. Draw a delete line through the incorrect marks. Write the correct ones above them.

Example: Have you ever been to Cedar Point? ~~.~~

Have you ever hunted for diamonds. Visitors to the Crater of Diamonds State Park in Murfreesboro, Arkansas, do every day. This is the only diamond field in the United States that is open to the public. How can you tell a diamond from an ordinary crystal. Experienced treasure seekers know that diamonds have a slick, oily surface that dirt or mud will not stick to. They keep their eyes opened for clean crystals. About 1,000 diamonds are found each year. Wow.

Practice

Write a paragraph to describe what is happening in the picture. Use question marks and exclamation points in the paragraph.

_____

_____

_____

_____

_____

Tips for Your Own Writing: Revising ....

Choose a piece of your own writing. Rewrite some of the sentences to use question marks and exclamation points.

 There certainly is a lot to learn about punctuation!

25

11 Punctuation: End Marks

✎ *Follow the sentence trend . . . with periods, question marks, or exclamation points, sentences should end.*

Did You Know?

A period ends a sentence that is a statement.

Broccoli is a vegetable that is rich in vitamins A and C**.**

A question mark ends a sentence that asks a question.

Do you know anyone who likes broccoli**?**

An exclamation point ends a sentence that expresses strong feelings.

I love broccoli**!**

Show What You Know

Add the correct end marks to each sentence. Circle the periods that you add.

Who invented chewing gum Gum was first used by Native Americans They boiled tree sap and let it dry in the sun This hardened, unflavored sap was called chicle

William Wrigley, Jr., made chewing gum an American favorite What is your favorite flavor of gum My favorite is spearmint gum It's great Wow, more than 500 companies make gum today

Score: _____   Total Possible: 9

Proofread

Four of the following sentences have incorrect end punctuation. Draw a delete line through the incorrect marks and write the correct ones above them.

Example: Did you know a tomato is a fruit.~~?~~

Do you know who created Mickey Mouse and Donald Duck! Walt Disney was responsible for making these cartoon characters famous. His company made the first cartoon of Mickey Mouse in 1928? After becoming successful in both films and television, Disney began opening theme parks. Have you ever been to Disneyland or Walt Disney World. They're great vacation spots?

Practice

Write two sentences about the picture. Use periods, question marks, or exclamation points.

1. _____

_____

2. _____

_____

Tips for Your Own Writing: Proofreading . . . .

Choose a piece of your own writing. Carefully check it for correct end marks. Make corrections where necessary.

Yes, positively! I need an explanation. Is this a statement, a question, or an exclamation?

12 Punctuation: Sentences I

Sentences are hard to understand when the writer doesn't add end marks where they belong.

Did You Know?

Sometimes two or more sentences are written as though they were one sentence. The end marks are not placed at the end of each sentence where they belong.

I am taller than Mary Beth is taller than I.

Jerry was playing tennis balls were everywhere.

One way to correct such groups of words is to separate them into two sentences with the correct end marks. Make sure to capitalize the first letter of the second sentence.

I am taller than Mary. Beth is taller than I.

Jerry was playing tennis. Balls were everywhere.

Show What You Know

Draw lines to show where each sentence should be separated.

Example: I have a best friend | his name is Antonio.

Duke Ellington was a famous composer, pianist, and band leader his favorite music was jazz. His band played at the Cotton Club in Harlem that is the section of New York City where Duke Ellington lived. Ellington's band became very popular in the 1930s the band traveled all over the country. Ellington was one of the founders of big-band jazz one of his most famous songs is "Mood Indigo."

Score: _____   Total Possible: 4

Proofread

Use the proper proofreading marks to show where end marks and capital letters should be used to correct four sentences.

Example: Pigs like to eat birds like to fly.

A terrarium is a tiny earth garden growing in glass I think plants would be very easy to grow this way. The plants inside the terrarium use the same water over and over again they are also protected from pollution. The temperature in the terrarium stays the same insects cannot feed on the plants. Doesn't this sound like a foolproof way to grow plants I'm going to give it a try.

Practice

Write a paragraph about what is happening in the picture. Use different kinds of end marks.

_____

_____

_____

_____

Tips for Your Own Writing: Proofreading ....

Choose a piece of your own writing. Check to make sure that the sentences are punctuated correctly.

_R_un along to the next lesson to find out more about punctuating sentences!

13 Punctuation: Sentences II

✏️ *Sometimes sentences run on and on and on and they never seem to stop or do they?*

Did You Know?

Sometimes groups of words are put together that belong in two separate sentences. They might be two or more sentences put together without punctuation, or they might be connected with a comma and with the words *and, or,* or *but*.

Incorrect punctuation: This is my pet fish make quiet pets.

Corrected punctuation: This is my pet. Fish make quiet pets.

Incorrect punctuation: These are my cat's kittens that I like to pet and aren't they cute?

Corrected punctuation: These are my cat's kittens that I like to pet. Aren't they cute?

Incorrect punctuation: It is raining, do not let the dog outside.

Corrected punctuation: It is raining. Do not let the dog outside.

Show What You Know

Draw lines to show where each sentence should be separated. Cross out unneeded words such as *and*.

My name is Dumpty Humpty and I had a brother named Humpty Dumpty.

One day Humpty Dumpty was sitting on a wall he fell he had a great fall. I

didn't want Humpty Dumpty to get hurt but he was hurt and he was broken.

Score: _____   Total Possible: 8

Proofread

Use the proper proofreading marks to show where four end marks and capital letters should be added to create correct sentences. Draw a delete line through two commas and the word *and* twice where necessary.

Example: I like to go to amusement parks and swimming at a pool is also fun.

Do you think that snakes are creepy, slimy creatures, if so, you have probably never met a snake up close. Snakes are reptiles and they are cold-blooded animals, and cold-blooded animals have body temperatures that change with the temperature of the environment. Snakes keep warm by lying in the sun they cool off by hiding in the shade.

Practice

Snakes are very interesting animals. Use an encyclopedia or another reference book to read about them. Then write a paragraph about snakes. Reread your sentences to check for correct punctuation.

_____

_____

_____

_____

Tips for Your Own Writing: Proofreading . . . .

Choose a piece of your own writing. Read it aloud to check sentences. Correct any sentences that should be separated by using correct end marks and capital letters.

Correct end marks will put an end to incorrect sentences!

14 Punctuation: Sentence Fragments I

Are sentence fragments pieces of broken sentences?

.... Did You Know?...................

A sentence always has at least two parts. One part tells what happened or what is.

cut the grass   **walked the dog**

The other part tells who or what is involved.

She cut the grass.   **Miguel** walked the dog.

A group of words that is only part of a sentence is called a *sentence fragment*. A sentence fragment is missing something.

It can be missing the part that tells who or what, or what happened.

Fragment: On the way home.

Sentence: She walked with Alesha on the way home.

Fragment: Rained all day long.

Sentence: We saw a rainbow after it rained all day.

Show What You Know

Read each group of words below. If it is a complete sentence, write *S* on the line. If it is a fragment, write *F* on the line.

1. Yellowstone was the first national park in the world.   _____

2. Known for spouting geysers and hot springs.   _____

3. The park is located in Wyoming, Idaho, and Montana.   _____

4. The park with beautiful scenery.   _____

5. You can still see wild bison in Yellowstone.   _____

6. See bison in a park.   _____

Score: _____   Total Possible: 6

Proofread

There are three sentence fragments in the paragraph below. Draw a line through the fragments. Write a complete sentence for each fragment on the lines below.

Example: ~~On our trip.~~ On our trip we saw a huge whale.

Tomorrow we are going to Yellowstone Park. Because "Old Faithful." I hope to see moose, bears, and wolves. Get there. We are going hiking. After hiking for a few hours. We are planning to stay for a week.

1. _____

2. _____

3. _____

Practice

Imagine that you are on the camping trip. Use complete sentences to write a paragraph about your trip.

_____

_____

_____

_____

Tips for Your Own Writing: Revising..........................

Choose three sentences you have written. Ask a partner to make sure each sentence makes sense by itself. Rewrite any fragments.

 A careful writer never leaves any loose pieces!

15 Punctuation: Sentence Fragments II

If your sentences are falling apart, they may be fragments.

···················· Did You Know? ·····················

A group of words that is only a part of a sentence is called a *sentence fragment*. Sometimes you can combine a sentence fragment with a sentence to make a complete sentence.

Sentence and fragment: We stayed at the park. Until it started to rain.

Corrected sentence: We stayed at the park until it started to rain.

Fragment and sentence: When Theresa picked us up. We were happy to find dry clothes in the car.

Corrected sentence: When Theresa picked us up, we were happy to find dry clothes in the car.

Show What You Know

Combine a sentence fragment from column A with a sentence from column B to make a complete sentence. Write the sentences on the lines below. Put a comma after the fragment from Column A.

A	B
To see Africa's highest mountain	Kibo is the highest peak.
At about 19,000 feet high	You must go to Mount Kilimanjaro.

1. _____

2. _____

Score: _____ **Total Possible: 2**

Proofread

Combine two sentences with sentence fragments to make complete sentences. Where needed, draw a delete line through the periods and add commas above them. Draw lines through capital letters that should not be capitalized.

Example: Tom ran after the ball. Before it landed in the creek.

Until World War I ended. Most American families did not have a bathtub. Most people did not take a bath every day. Because they did not think it was a healthy thing to do. Early bathtubs were made of wood, metal, or rubber. Modern bathtubs became popular after 1920.

Practice

Add words to make the fragments into complete sentences.

1. **When I grow up,** _____.

2. _____ **which is my favorite subject at school.**

3. **Since I want to learn to dance,** _____.

4. **Last year when I visited my aunt,** _____.

Tips for Your Own Writing: Revising...........................

Choose a piece of your own writing. Read it over carefully and look for sentence fragments. Rewrite any fragments to make them into complete sentences.

Sometimes your mind works faster than your hand. Take the time to write complete sentences!

16 Review: End Marks

A. There are nine periods missing in the letter below. Use proofreading marks to show where periods are needed.

7541 Black Oak Ave

Wolfville, Storyland

June 25, 1996

Dear Mr and Mrs Piggy,

    My sisters and I are planning a barbecue dinner on July 10, 1996. We have invited everyone from our neighborhood. Ms Bo Peep, Rev Wily Fox, and Dr Mary Lamb will be coming. Dr Patricia Wolf will begin cooking at 2 o'clock. Please plan on attending. We would love to have you for dinner

        Sincerely,

        Big B Wolf

Score: _____   Total Possible: 9

B. Use proofreading marks to show where 12 periods are needed in the paragraphs.

    Have you ever read the poem that tells how many days are in each month? It says that there are 30 days in Sept, Apr, June, and Nov It then says all the rest such as Dec have 31 days except one month. That is Feb, which has 28 days in most years.

    There is also a poem that names the days of the week. It begins by saying that Mon has a child that is fair of face. All other days of the week—Tues, Wed, Thurs, Fri, Sat, and Sun—are mentioned. These poems can help you remember how many days are in each month and the names of the days of the week.

Score: _____   Total Possible: 12

C. Add two periods, four question marks, and two exclamation points where needed.

Did you know that sometimes two birds of the same kind look very different The male bird is covered with bright, beautiful feathers Can these bright markings attract female birds You bet they can Why does the female bird have dull, drab feathers Those dull feathers are really a built-in protection Can enemies see her sitting on her nest of eggs They absolutely cannot

Score: _____   Total Possible: 8

D. Delete unnecessary words such as *and*. Use the proper proofreading marks to show three capital letters, and add four end marks to correct sentences.

According to legend, the Olympics began in ancient times they were started by a Greek man named Hercules. Hercules and his three brothers ran a foot race and Hercules won the race and the Greeks decided to hold more contests to honor Hercules. The Greeks held the contest once every four years now the summer and winter Olympics take place alternately every two years.

Score: _____   Total Possible: 9

E. Use the proper proofreading marks to correct sentence fragments by taking out unnecessary punctuation. Draw a line through letters that should not be capitalized. Add one missing comma.

1. I think year-round school is a good idea. Because it makes better use of the buildings and staff.
2. When kids take computer classes over the summer. They learn new skills.

Score: _____   Total Possible: 5

REVIEW SCORE: _____   REVIEW TOTAL: 43

17 Punctuation: Commas in Series and Introductions

Your audience will give applause if you use commas to show a pause.

.... Did You Know?........................

A comma follows each item in a series except the last one.

> New York, Philadelphia, and Chicago have well-known city parks.

A comma follows an introductory word or phrase to separate it from the rest of the sentence.

> Yes, Central Park is in New York.
> Before the concert, people waited in the park.

A comma is used to show a pause you would make if you were saying the sentence aloud.

> We planned a picnic in the park, but we had to cancel it because of the rain.

Show What You Know

Read the report below. Add commas after each word in a series and after introductory words.

There once was a Russian who made beautiful eggs for the czar, or ruler of Russia. Carl Fabergé made eggs that were covered with gold silver and other precious metals. Diamonds pearls and valuable jewels decorated other eggs. There was a surprise in each egg. A small golden carriage a diamond-studded flower basket or a royal crown may be found in a Fabergé egg. Today each egg is worth a great deal of money. Collectors own these special eggs, and they seldom offer the eggs for sale.

Score: _____   **Total Possible: 6**

Proofread

This paragraph on immigrants contains six mistakes in the use of commas. Use a caret to add commas where they are needed.

Example: No, I do not like to play soccer.

    Between 1880 and 1923, 23 million people came to the United States. Most of these people came from Germany Ireland, Poland and Italy. Many left because there was not enough work in their country. Land in the United States was very cheap and there were many jobs in this country. After arriving in the United States immigrants often settled in areas with other people from their homelands. Areas like Chinatown Little Italy and Greektown sprang up in cities all across the United States.

Practice

On another piece of paper, write a letter to a friend telling about things you would like to do during summer vacation. Use sentences that list things in a series. Use an introductory word like *yes, no,* or *well* to begin one sentence.

Tips for Your Own Writing: Revising ....

Choose a piece of your own writing. Rewrite it by adding names, action words, or descriptive words in a series. Make sure you use commas to separate the words in a series.

Yes, it is true! Using commas can make your writing clear, understandable, and easy to read.

18 Punctuation: Friendly Letters

Sure, it is an open and closed case because commas in letters set the pace.

······················ **Did You Know?**······················

A comma is used between the city and state in the heading.

Plano, Texas   Eugene, Oregon   Slidell, Louisiana

A comma is placed between the day and the year in the heading.

April 22, 1996 November 10, 1989 January 3, 1997

A comma is used after the last word in the greeting.

Dear Tony,   My dearest Grandmother,

To my classmates,

A comma is placed after the last word in the closing.

Sincerely,   Your best friend,   Very truly yours,

··

Show What You Know

Add commas where they are necessary.

1. Mequon Wisconsin
2. February 14 1996
3. Dear Uncle George
4. Yours truly
5. To my students
6. With love
7. Sacramento California
8. Dear Luis
9. Grimsley Tennessee
10. Your best friend

Score: _____   **Total Possible: 10**

Proofread

Four commas are missing in the friendly letter below. Use the proper proofreading marks to insert the commas where they are needed.

Example: My favorite aunt lives in New Boston‸Michigan.

---

652 Applegate Circle
Lake Zurich Illinois 60047
May 25 1996

Dear Grady

    Thanks for taking care of our pets while we were on vacation. The hike through the Grand Canyon was awesome.
    You can count on me to take care of your dog when you go to hockey camp next month.

                    Thanks again

                    Marietta

Practice

On another piece of paper, write a friendly letter to a friend thanking him or her for a gift or favor you have received. Make sure to use commas correctly in the letter.

Tips for Your Own Writing: Proofreading ....

The next time you write a letter, check to make sure that commas have been used correctly. Add commas where they are needed.

Use commas between the city and state and in a date. Also, use a comma to greet and close.

19 Punctuation: Commas in Dialogue

To separate who said what in a quotation, commas are the punctuation of notation.

······················· **Did You Know?**·····················

When you write a conversation between two or more persons, you are writing a dialogue. Use a comma before and after the speaker's words to separate them from the rest of the sentence.

The teacher asked, "What's round on both ends and high in the middle?"

His students answered, "Ohio!"

Dennis said, "I don't like cheese with holes in it."

"Then don't eat the holes, dear," said Grandma.

Show What You Know

Read the jokes below. Add commas to separate the speaker's words from the rest of the sentence.

1. Julie asked "Why are you taking oats to bed with you?"
2. "To feed my night-mare" answered Bill.

3. "Eat your spinach. It puts color into your cheeks" said Aunt Ellen.
4. Cousin Kyle answered "Who wants green cheeks?"

5. Carley Cat asked "How will I make ends meet?"
6. "Just put your tail into your mouth" advised Melvin Mouse.

7. Paul said "Are there any letters in the mailbox?"
8. "No, they're all in the alphabet" replied Pedro.

Score: _____   Total Possible: 8

Proofread

Use four proofreading marks to add commas to these sentences.

Example: Pablo asked‸"When are we leaving for the movies?"

Gary asked "Do you know why a tulip closes up at night?"

"At night the flower feels cold air and closes its petals" said Gloria Gardenia.

Mr. Greenthumb explained "When the warm morning sun arrives, the tulip opens again."

Gloria Gardenia added "You know, tulips also close up on cool, rainy days!"

Practice

Study the picture. Write a dialogue for the two girls talking about a movie. Use commas to separate the speaker's words from the rest of the sentence.

_____

_____

_____

_____

_____

Tips for Your Own Writing: Revising ....

Choose a paragraph from your own writing. Rewrite it as a dialogue using commas to separate the speaker's words from the rest of the sentence.

"Use a comma to separate what was said from who said it," she said.

20 Punctuation: Quotation Marks in Dialogue

You can mark my words and yours with quotation marks.

·················· Did You Know? ··················

A quotation is the exact words that someone says. It always begins and ends with quotation marks. Quotation marks look like this: " ".

Marty asked, "Why do elephants have such big ears?"

"Elephants live in hot climates with few trees and need to find a way to cool off," said Dr. Bell.

The end marks and commas are placed inside the quotation marks.

Marty continued, "I still don't understand how big ears can help."

"When an elephant flaps its ears, it releases body warmth into the air," explained Dr. Bell.

Show What You Know

Read the dialogue below. Use " and " to show where the quotation marks should be used before and after each speaker's words.

That was quite a joke Aunt Angela played on us, said Miguel to Ana.

Ana laughed, It certainly was. I was kind of afraid to open the envelope when I saw that it said there were rattlesnake eggs in it.

I was, too, but we should have known better, said Miguel.

Ana agreed, Yes, we should have known rattlesnakes don't lay eggs.

Right, I really jumped, though, when we started to open the envelope and heard the rattling noise, said Miguel.

Score: _____   Total Possible: 10

Proofread

Use four proofreading marks to show where quotation marks are needed.

Example: "No running on deck!" shouted the lifeguard.

"I think we should go to Washington for our vacation, Scott said.

The White House is the most beautiful building in the United States, he announced.

Maura added, "Seeing the cherry blossoms in bloom along the Potomac River is an unforgettable sight.

Practice

Make up a conversation between you and a visitor from another place. Have each speaker try to convince the other that his or her hometown is the best place to live. Use quotation marks to show the exact words of each speaker.

_____

_____

_____

_____

_____

Tips for Your Own Writing: Revising ....

Choose two sentences that you have written. Rewrite them using quotations. Use commas to separate the speaker's words from other parts of each sentence.

✏️ *Remember, when writing people's remarks, use quotation marks!*

21 Punctuation: Quotation Marks and Commas in Dialogue

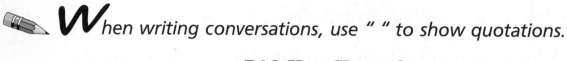 **W**hen writing conversations, use " " to show quotations.

.... Did You Know?.....................

Quotation marks are used when a writer repeats a speaker's words exactly. They are always used in pairs. Quotation marks go right before and right after what the speaker says.

"Mrs. Burns left you a message," said Dad.

If the quotation does not end the sentence, you need to use a comma to mark the end of the speaker's words. Make sure the comma is inside the quotation mark.

"I'm going to give LingLing a bath," announced Mai.

If the quotation does not begin the sentence, use a comma to separate the first part of the sentence from the quotation. In these kinds of sentences, place the comma before the first quotation mark.

Uncle Henry said, "There's a storm coming."

Show What You Know

Read the paragraph below. Add quotation marks and commas where they are needed. Be sure to place commas and quotation marks in the correct order.

Ms. Carter announced, Today, Mary is going to tell us about something that happened to her.

Mary stood and said "My lamb followed me to school.

Will he make us laugh and play? asked Little Boy Blue.

Score: _____   Total Possible: 6

Proofread

Use proofreading marks where they are needed. Add three commas and six quotation marks.

Example: "That ride was too short, said Scott.

I had been asleep about an hour last night when I heard the funniest little

sounds" said Monica.

I asked What did it sound like?

Monica said, "It was kind of like a bunch of little squeaks."

"What was it? I demanded.

Monica exclaimed Winnie had her kittens!

Practice

Pretend that you are talking to your favorite cartoon character. Write your conversation. Make sure to include both the questions and the answers in quotation marks.

_____

_____

_____

_____

Tips for Your Own Writing: Proofreading ....

Find a piece of your own writing. Check to make sure that you have set off the speaker's words by using quotation marks.

**W**hen writing someone's words, make sure you keep on track by placing quotation marks at the front and back.

22 Punctuation: Quotation Marks in Titles

Use quotation marks with a story's name. For a poem, use them just the same.

.... Did You Know? ....

Use quotation marks around the titles of reports, stories, and poems.

It seems like every year I write a report called "My Best Summer Vacation."

Terrence read his story "The Day I Met an Amazing Alien" to the class.

I wrote a poem called "The Whispering Pine Tree."

Only use quotation marks when you are writing about the work in a sentence. Do not put quotation marks around the title when it appears on the first page or cover of the work.

Kelly wrote a poem about the weather. She called it "Rain."

Rain
by Kelly Buckley

Show What You Know

Add quotation marks around the titles of stories, reports, and poems in the sentences below.

Paul Revere's Ride was written by Henry Wadsworth Longfellow. I called my report Heroes of the Revolutionary War. Cara's report, Betsy Ross and the American Flag, was the most interesting. Yankee Doodle has been a popular American song since the 1700s. The Green Mountain Boys is a story about soldiers from Vermont who fought for the American Colonies.

Score: _____   Total Possible: 10

Proofread

Three titles in the paragraph below are missing quotation marks. Use the proper proofreading marks to add them where they are needed.

Example: I called my story "The Mysterious Closet."

Principal Dodds decided to host a public-speaking contest to help the students of Oak Creek School overcome stage fright. Each student picked a favorite story or poem to recite. Tim Weaver recited the poem Inside Turtle's Shell. Amanda Jones told the Polynesian legend Why Most Trees and Plants Have Flat Leaves. Ted Redwing told a Native American story How the People Sang Up the Mountains.

Practice

Find your favorite poem. Then write a paragraph telling why you like that particular poem. Be sure to tell the name of the poem. Share your writing with the class.

_____

_____

_____

Tips for Your Own Writing: Proofreading ....

Find a piece of your own writing that has titles of stories, poems, or reports. Check to make sure that you remembered to use quotation marks.

With stories and poems, both short and long, quotation marks sometimes belong.

23 Punctuation: Underlining in Book Titles

When writing the title of a book, use underlining for the right look.

.... **Did You Know?** ....

Printers put the title of a book in *italics* to set it off from the rest of the sentence. You may be able to use italics when writing with a computer.

> Frank L. Baum wrote *The Wonderful Wizard of Oz* in 1900.

When you write the title of a book, you can set it off from the rest of the sentence by underlining it.

> The Wonderful Wizard of Oz is still popular with young readers today.

Show What You Know

Read each sentence below. Underline the titles.

1. Little Navajo Bluebird is a book about a girl who refuses to abandon the customs of her people.

2. Harry Allard's book Miss Nelson Is Missing has a surprise ending.

3. Ramona the Pest is one of a series of books that Beverly Cleary wrote about a girl named Ramona.

4. Ragtime Tumpie is an award-winning book by Alan Schroeder.

5. Tacky the Penguin is an animal fantasy by Helen Lester.

6. Toy animals come to life in A. A. Milne's book Winnie the Pooh.

7. Dick King-Smith tells about an unusual kitten in Martin's Mice.

8. The book The Bracelet by Yoshiko Uchida is about a Japanese-American family during World War II.

Score: _____   Total Possible: 8

Proofread

Read the letter below. Underline the three titles.

Example: I loved reading <u>Iggie's House</u>.

---

136 Sunnybrook Circle
Panama Beach, Florida 36890
October 10, 1996

Dear Aunt Claire,

    I was cleaning out my bookshelf and found some books that Lynne might enjoy. When I was her age, <u>Madeline</u> was my favorite book. Since she's in first grade, she might like <u>Frog and Toad Are Friends</u>. By the end of the year, she'll be ready to tackle <u>Two Good Friends</u>. I hope Lynne enjoys these books as much as I did!

        Your niece,

        Michelle

Practice

Make a list of your favorite books. Be sure to underline the titles. Share your list with your classmates.

_____

_____

_____

_____

Tips for Your Own Writing: Proofreading ....

Find a piece of your own writing that has titles of books in it. Check to make sure that you have underlined them.

✏️ ***N**ow you know to underline the name of your favorite book or mine!*

24 Review: Commas, Quotation Marks, Underlining

A. Use the proper proofreading marks to add ten commas to separate items in a series in each sentence below.

The three largest continents are Asia Africa and North America. Africa has many kinds of land including grassy plains tropical rain forests and the world's largest desert. Nigeria Egypt and Ethiopia have the greatest populations among African nations. In Africa, there are copper diamond and gold mines. Some African farmers grow cassava cocoa beans and yams.

Score: _____   **Total Possible: 10**

B. Four commas are missing in the friendly letter below. Use the proper proofreading marks to insert the commas where they are needed.

712 E. 42nd Street
Albany New York
August 20 1996

Dear Mrs. Kiefer

Thank you so much for taking our gymnastics team to Atlanta last month. I still can't believe that I saw world-class gymnasts competing in the Olympics. I'm looking forward to working with you and the other team members this year.

Sincerely

Kelly McLoughlin

Score: _____   **Total Possible: 4**

C. **Read each sentence below. Use three proofreading marks to show where commas should be used to separate the speaker's words from the rest of the sentence.**

1. "Please let me stay up late tonight" I begged my parents.
2. "You know that tomorrow is a school day" my mom reminded me.
3. I explained "This will be my only chance to see the comet."

Score: _____   Total Possible: 3

D. **There are eight mistakes in quotation marks and two missing commas in the paragraph below. If quotation marks or commas are missing, use the proper proofreading marks to add them. If there are quotation marks where they are not needed, delete them.**

Heidi asked, Is Dave off at practice again?

Yes, he goes to the rink each morning at five and practices two hours after school each night Dave's Aunt Helen replied.

"Heidi knew Dave never missed a chance to practice his skating." She said Well, I guess Dave knows that practice makes perfect!

Score: _____   Total Possible: 10

E. **Use six proofreading marks to add quotation marks around the titles of stories, reports, and poems in the paragraph below.**

I called my health class report The Five Food Groups. My dad thought that Eating Your Way Around the World would be a catchy title. Grandpa gave me a poem he wrote about eating called Down the Hatch.

Score: _____   Total Possible: 6

F. **Read the paragraph below. Find and underline the four book titles.**

I love to read scary books. Some of my favorite books are It Came from Beneath the Sink, Night of the Living Dummy, and Mostly Monsters. My older brother says The Phantom of the Opera gives him chills.

Score: _____   Total Possible: 4

REVIEW SCORE: _____   REVIEW TOTAL: 37

25 Usage: Verbs–Do, Have

How do you do? I do fine, but he does fine.

.... **Did You Know?** ....

Each sentence has two parts: the subject and the verb. The subject tells who or what does or is. The verb tells what the subject does or is. The subject and the verb must work together.

Some verbs have different forms depending on the subject.

Do		Have	
I **do**	we **do**	I **have**	we **have**
you **do**	they **do**	you **have**	they **have**
he, she, it **does**		he, she, it **has**	

He **does** his homework in his room.
He **has** a computer on his desk.
I **do** not own a computer.
We **have** to use the computers at school.

....

Show What You Know

Underline the incorrect form of the verb in each sentence. Write the correct form above.

1. We has a big old house.

2. Dad do the outdoor painting.

3. Mom and Heidi does the trim.

4. The house have ten windows.

5. The windows has many panes.

6. I does the mowing.

7. My brother do the raking.

8. They has a barbecue.

Score: _____   **Total Possible: 16**

Proofread

There are five mistakes in using the verbs *do/does* and *has/have* in the paragraph below. Use proofreading marks to delete each incorrect word and write the correct word above it.

Example: He ~~do~~ does the dishes after dinner.

We all have red hair. My dad and mom does, my little brother does, and my two sisters does. My mom and brother has hair the color of tomatoes. Dad have hair the color of carrots. My sisters do, too. People say I'm lucky because I has hair that is called "strawberry blond."

Practice

Fill in the name of your community in the blank line of the first sentence in your news story. Then finish the story. Use *do, does, has,* and *have.* Share your news story with your classmates.

Today was a big day for the town of _____.

_____

_____

_____

_____

_____

Tips for Your Own Writing: Proofreading ....

Next time you write, use the reminder that **h**e, **i**t, **s**he (**his**) take *does* and *has*. Other pronouns take *do* and *have*.

The form of do *or* have *depends on who is having or doing. Check on their forms when you're reviewing.*

26 Usage: Verbs–Am, Is, Are, Was, Were

Verbs are sometimes tricky! But you don't need to be a magician to learn how to make subjects and verbs get along!

.... Did You Know? ....

The verbs *am, is, are, was,* and *were* are all forms of the verb *be.* The verb *be* does not show action. It tells what someone or something is or is like.

Am, is, and *are* tell what someone or something is now.

> I **am** an artist.   He **is** an artist.   You **are** an artist.

Was and *were* tell what someone or something was in the past.

> She **was** a swimmer.   You **were** a swimmer.
> They **were** all swimmers.   You **were** all swimmers.

Use *am, is,* and *was* with *I, she, he,* and *it.*

> I **am**   she **is**   he **is**   it **is**
> I **was**   she **was**   he **was**   it **was**

Use *are* and *were* with *we, they,* and *you.*

> we **are**   they **are**   we **were**   they **were**
> you **are**   you **were**

· ·

Show What You Know

Write *is* or *are* in each blank to correctly complete each sentence below.

My teachers _____ Mr. Clark and Ms. Juliano. Our school _____ in Fort
₁   ₂
Lauderdale, Florida. Luis Mendoza _____ our class president. There _____ only
₃   ₄
21 students in our class. Most of the students _____ girls. Mr. Eilert, our
₅
principal, _____ the greatest! The teachers _____ pretty cool, too!
₆   ₇

Score: _____   Total Possible: 7

Proofread

There are six mistakes in the use of the verb *be* in the paragraph below. Use proofreading marks to delete each incorrect word and write the correct word above it.

Example: We ~~is~~ on the baseball team.

(are written above "is")

Michael Jordan was one of the most exciting athletes in the world today. He is born in Brooklyn, New York, and grew up in Wilmington, North Carolina. When he was a freshman at the University of North Carolina, he made the winning shot in the 1982 NCAA championship game. He were a member of both the 1984 and 1992 Olympic basketball teams. He are known for his acrobatic dunk shots. Michael are a six-foot six-inch player for the Chicago Bulls. The Bulls was the national champions of 1996.

Practice

Write a paragraph about yourself. Use the verbs *am*, *is*, *are*, *was*, and *were*.

_____

_____

_____

_____

_____

Tips for Your Own Writing: Proofreading ....

Begin to keep a journal. Proofread your entries to make sure you used *am*, *is*, and *are* to show present time and *was* or *were* to show past time.

With the verb be, *you are sure to go far if you use* was *and* were *when it happened in the past; but in the present, you use* am, is, *and* are.

A. Write the correct form of the verb on each of the lines below.

1. Larry _____ thirty sit-ups every day. (does, do)

2. He _____ them so that he will get stronger. (does, do)

3. He also _____ a set of weights in his basement. (have, has)

4. Lee and Lance _____ a treadmill. (have, has)

5. It _____ adjustable speeds. (have, has)

6. Lee _____ a workout three times a week. (does, do)

7. Lance _____ no time for exercise. (have, has)

8. He always says, "I'll _____ it tomorrow." (does, do)

Score: _____   Total Possible: 8

B. Complete each sentence in the paragraph below by writing a subject noun or pronoun on the line. Make sure your subject works with the underlined verb.

_____ <u>does</u> the cooking at Jeremy's house. _____
              1   2

<u>has</u> no time to cook anymore. _____ <u>have</u> a big country kitchen.
                                                       3

_____ <u>has</u> a microwave oven, refrigerator, and two stoves.
              4

_____ <u>have</u> big appetites. _____ <u>have</u> dinner at 6:30
              5   6

every night. _____ <u>do</u> the dishes.
                             7

Score: _____   Total Possible: 7

C. Underline the verb in each of the eight sentences below. Then write _present_ or _past_ on the line to tell which tense the verb is.

1. Brian Long is a reporter for the _Newton News._   _____

2. The _News_ is the largest paper in southern Missouri.   _____

3. Brian's first story was about a fire in a factory.   _____

4. Five fire trucks were on the scene.   _____

5. Fifty people were in the factory.   _____

6. Brian was able to report some good news.   _____

7. Firemen were able to control the flames.   _____

8. All the people were rescued.   _____

Score: _____   Total Possible: 16

D. Each sentence is written to show present time. Use proofreading marks to delete the seven verbs in the sentences below. Add new verbs above each one to show past time.

Mildred Didrikson is an American athlete who was born in Port Arthur, Texas, in 1914. Didrikson is nicknamed "Babe" in honor of Babe Ruth, a famous baseball player.

Babe is a member of the Golden Cyclones basketball team. They are national champions. Babe is a gold-medal track star in the 1932 Olympic Games. People are also proud of Babe's fourteen golf tournament victories. She is the outstanding woman athlete of the first half of the twentieth century.

Score: _____   Total Possible: 7

REVIEW SCORE: _____   REVIEW TOTAL: 38

28 Usage: Verbs–Sang, Ran

I sang while I ran, although I have never sung and run at the same time before.

.... **Did You Know?** ....

Sang and sung and ran and run are pairs of verbs that give some writers trouble.

Sang and ran tell about something that happened in the past.

> The Cat Club **sang** in our street until midnight.
> When my angry dad opened the door, they **ran** away.

Sung and run also tell about something that happened in the past. They are used with helping words like *have, has, had,* and *could have*. They tell about something that has happened over a period of time or that might have happened.

> The cats **could have sung** all night long.
> They **have run** away, but they come back.

....

Show What You Know

Read the paragraph below. Write the correct verb (*ran* or *run*) in each blank.

My mom and I _____ in a marathon race last week. It was the first time
          1
we had _____ a long race. I could have _____ last year, but I didn't think I
          2   3
was strong enough. I _____ the 26 miles in just over six hours. I could have
                          4
_____ faster, but I didn't want to leave Mom behind.
 5

Score: _____   Total Possible: 5

Proofread

If the underlined verb is not used correctly, use proofreading marks to delete it. Then write the correct verb above it. There are six incorrect verbs.

Example: She <u>sang</u> the same song he had <s><u>sang</u></s> ~~sung~~ yesterday.

The Whittier School Chorus <u>sung</u> for our local cable show yesterday. They
₁

had <u>sang</u> many times before with no problem. However, this was the first
₂

time they had <u>sang</u> on TV. First, Corey <u>sang</u> his solo. He forgot the words!
₃ ₄

Mindy and Myra had <u>sang</u> their duet many times before. This time they <u>sung</u>
₅ ₆

way off-key. The show ended after the chorus <u>sung</u> the same song three times
₇

in a row. They never got the words right once!

Practice

Write two sentences using *sang* and *sung* or *ran* and *run.* Use each word once. Exchange your sentences with a classmate. Read the sentences aloud.

1. _____

_____

2. _____

Tips for Your Own Writing: Revising ....

The next time you write about something that happened in the past, make sure you use helping words with *sung* or *run.*

If it happened over a period of time or might have happened, a little help from has *or* have *is needed for* sung *or* run.

29 Usage: Verbs—Wore, Done

✏ *I wore my favorite jeans today and yesterday. I could have worn them every day this week.*

Did You Know?

Wore and *worn* and *did* and *done* are pairs of verbs that give some writers trouble.

Wore and *did* tell about something that happened in the past.

Worn and *done* tell about something that has happened over a period of time or that might have happened. They are used with helping words like *have*, *has*, *had*, and *could have*.

I **wore** my raincoat to school today.
I **have worn** my raincoat every day this week.
I **could have worn** my sweater today.
I **did** my social studies report on Chief Joseph.
I **have done** reports before.
I **could have done** a report on any leader I wanted.

Show What You Know

For each sentence, choose the correct verb in parentheses and write it on the line.

1. The pioneers _____ many new things on the prairie. (did, done)

2. They had never _____ some of those things before. (did, done)

3. When their clothes _____ out, they had to make new ones. (wore, worn)

4. Men _____ hunting shirts made from deerskin. (wore, worn)

5. Women wove the fabric to make the dresses they _____. (wore, worn)

Score: _____   Total Possible: 5

Proofread

The note below has five mistakes in the use of *wore, worn, did,* and *done.* Use proofreading marks to delete each incorrect verb and write the correct verb above it.

Example: I d̶o̶n̶e̶ my job quickly.
(did written above done)

> Dear Jenny,
>
> You won't believe what I done last month. I tried out for a
> part in a movie. I have never did anything like that before.
> When I tried out, I worn my sneakers. The movie people asked
> if I could have run as fast if I had wore dress shoes. Mom told
> them I could run that fast even if I worn no shoes at all.
>
> Your friend,
>
> *Enrico*

Practice

Write two sentences about the people in the picture. Use *wore* and *worn* or *did* and *done.* Use helping words with *worn* and *done.*

1. _____

_____

2. _____

_____

Tips for Your Own Writing: Proofreading ....

Don't forget to use helping words when you use *done* and *worn.*

 Are you wore/worn out yet?

30 Usage: Verbs—Gave, Went

Give this lesson a chance to help you with some irregular verbs.

.... **Did You Know?** ....

Gave and *went* **tell about something that happened in the past.**

Given and *gone* **also tell about something that happened in the past. Anytime you use** *given* **and** *gone,* **you need to use a helping word.** *Have, has, had, was,* **and** *were* **are helping words.**

Mai **gave** the skates to me.
Van **had given** Mai the skates.
They **were given** to Van from his friend.
Yesterday, we **went** to Sunset Park.
We **have never gone** there before.
We **were gone** before dark.

Show What You Know

Write the correct verb in the blank to complete each sentence.

1. We _____ to the Memorial Day parade. (went, gone)

2. We have _____ to the parade every year. (went, gone)

3. This year, the mayor _____ some soldiers special medals. (gave, given)

4. They had _____ to fight in Vietnam. (went, gone)

5. Many soldiers were _____ medals after the war. (gave, given)

6. Twenty-three soldiers from our village were _____ medals. (gave, given)

Score: _____   Total Possible: 6

Proofread

The paragraph below has four mistakes in using the verbs *gave*, *given*, *went*, and *gone*. Use proofreading marks to delete each incorrect verb and write the correct one above it.

Example: Last week we ~~gone~~ ^{went} skating at the park.

Every day, Old Mother Hubbard has gave her dog a bone. One day, she

gone to the cupboard to get a bone. To her surprise, there were none,

although yesterday she had bought a new package. Because she had no

bones, she given the dog some water. The dog then pushed open the pantry

door and found the bones he had hidden. He given one to the cat to eat.

Then he ate the rest. Now there really were none!

Practice

Write a thank-you note to someone who has given you something or who has done something for you. Use the words *gave*, *given*, *went*, and *gone*.

_____

_____

_____

_____

Tips for Your Own Writing: Proofreading ....

Make sure you use helping words with *given* and *gone* when you write. *Gave* and *went* do not need any help.

✏️ **H**ave you went/gone all out? Have you gave/given your best effort?

31 Usage: Verbs—Ate, Saw

You need a second helping (of helping words, that is!) when you use eaten *or* seen.

······························ **Did You Know?** ·····························

Ate and *saw* tell about something that happened in the past.

Eaten and *seen* also tell about something that happened in the past and are used with a helping word like *have, has, had,* or *would have.* They tell about something that might have happened or that did happen.

The spelling of some verbs changes when they tell about the past and follow a helping word.

I **ate** two oranges and two apples today.
I **should have eaten** some spinach or beans.
I **saw** you eat pizza yesterday.
I **have seen** you pick olives off your pizza.

Show What You Know

Write *ate* or *eaten* on the line to complete each sentence.

We _____ very different kinds of food on our trip to Japan. I had
      1

_____ fish many times, but it has always been cooked. We _____
  2   **3**

something called sushi that was made with raw fish. The Japanese have

_____ raw fish for centuries. They have always _____ different kinds of
  4   **5**

seaweed, too. On our last evening in Japan, we _____ fish and vegetables
                                                6

fried in batter. I liked that meal the best.

Score: _____   Total Possible: 6

Proofread

Use proper proofreading marks to delete four verbs in bold type that are incorrect. Write the correct verb above each one.

Example: We had ~~saw~~ ^{seen} that monument last year.

We **seen**₁ the most spectacular caves at the Carlsbad Caverns in New Mexico. I had never **saw**₂ such large underground rooms. We saw formations called stalagmites that looked like icicles growing up from the cavern's floor. We **seen**₃ some that had grown to be more than sixty feet tall. If we had walked farther into the cavern, we could have **saw**₄ a rock formation called the Bashful Elephant.

Practice

Write a paragraph about the best meal that you have ever eaten. Write about how the food looked and tasted. Use the words *ate*, *eaten*, *saw*, and *seen*.

_____

_____

_____

_____

_____

Tips for Your Own Writing: Proofreading

When you use the words *eaten* and *seen* in your writing, make sure you always give them help by using words such as *have*, *has*, and *had*.

If you have saw the mistake in this sentence, you understand this lesson.

32 Review: Verbs

A. Write the correct verb in the blanks from each pair of verbs in parentheses.

(sang, sung)

What was I going to do? Baby Lauren wouldn't go to sleep. I _____
1
every lullaby I knew. Then Grandma _____ a song from a commercial on TV.
2
Lauren went right to sleep. Grandma laughed, "I have _____ that song many
3
times. I know it works. Every time Grandpa hears it, he dozes right off!"

(ran, run)

The gust of wind caught Tito's kite and blew it high into the sky. Tito _____
4
over the hill, clenching his kite string in his hand. The kite continued to drift

toward the pond. When Tito had _____ as far as he could, he stopped. If he
5
_____ any farther, he would be knee-deep in water. He slowly let go of the kite.
6

Score: _____   Total Possible: 6

B. Write the correct verb in each blank.

1. Mrs. Cain _____ a good job making costumes for the play. (did, done)

2. Mia _____ a dress that looked just like a real queen's gown. (wore, worn)

3. Her red shoes had been _____ in last year's play. (wore, worn)

4. She also _____ a cape Mrs. Cain made from old curtains. (wore, worn)

5. Mrs. Cain had _____ a great job painting the scenery. (did, done)

Score: _____   Total Possible: 5

C. Write the correct verb—*gave, given, went,* or *gone*—in each blank. Then write four sentences of your own using each of the verbs.

1. Grandma and Grandpa _____ on a trip to Switzerland.

2. They had _____ to Ireland the year before.

3. They _____ each grandchild a cuckoo clock.

4. No one had ever _____ me such an unusual clock before.

1. _____

2. _____

3. _____

4. _____

Score: _____   Total Possible: 8

D. Choose a verb from those listed below to complete each sentence. Write the correct word in each blank.

ate	eaten	saw	seen

I thought I had _____ everything until I went to the Plainfield Pie Eating
                    1

Contest! I _____ some people eating apple, cherry, blueberry, and peach pies.
            2

Others _____ strawberry and banana cream pies. Some people _____ more
         3   4

than one. A few people had _____ pie since six in the morning. I _____ a slice
                             5   6

of chocolate cream pie. Then I saw something called shoofly pie. I would have

_____ a piece, but I usually don't eat bugs!
  7

Score: _____   Total Possible: 7

REVIEW SCORE: _____   REVIEW TOTAL: 26

33 Usage: Adjectives

Use bigger for two and biggest for more than two when comparing is what you want to do.

.... **Did You Know?** ....

Adjectives are words that describe nouns.

The ending -er is added to most adjectives that compare two people, places, or things. The ending -est is added to most adjectives to compare more than two people, places, or things.

A coyote can run **faster** than a bear.
The cheetah is the **fastest** animal of all.

If the adjective ends with an e, drop the e before adding the -er or -est ending.

large   larg**er**   larg**est**

If the adjective ends with a single vowel and a consonant, double the consonant and add the -er or -est ending.

big   big**ger**   big**gest**

If the adjective ends with a consonant and y, change the y to i before adding -er or -est.

tiny   tin**ier**   tin**iest**

Some long adjectives use more and most.

beautiful   **more** beautiful   **most** beautiful

Show What You Know

Write the correct adjective on each line.

1. We just had the _____ summer in history. (hotter, hottest)

2. Dad was _____ about the weather than we were. (happier, happiest)

3. His roses were _____ than ever. (more beautiful, most beautiful)

Score: _____   **Total Possible: 3**

Proofread

The paragraph below has five mistakes in adjectives that compare. Use proofreading marks to delete each incorrect adjective and write the correct one above it.

Example: We picked the ~~bigger~~ biggest apples in the orchard.

The larger trees in the world live in the Sequoia National Park in California. The park was created to protect these more amazing trees. Unlike other trees, the giant sequoia's trunk does not get thinner at the top. Some trees are widest than a city street. The taller tree in the park is 310 feet high. The tree called General Sherman is the overall bigger tree in the world. It weighs 6,000 tons and is still growing!

Practice

Write three sentences about the picture. Use adjectives like *busy, loud, quiet, small, slow,* and *happy.*

_____

_____

_____

_____

_____

Tips for Your Own Writing: Proofreading ....

When you are writing comparisons, think of the words *better* and *best*. The *-er* in *better* stands for two and the *-est* in *best* stands for more than two.

You couldn't do better if you did your best job on this lesson.

34 Usage: Homophones—Hear/Here, To/Too/Two

*H*ear! Hear! Here are two homophones that sound the same but are confusing, too—hear/here *and* to/too/two.

Did You Know?

Words that sound alike but that are spelled differently and have different meanings are called <u>**homophones.**</u>

Here **and** *hear* **are homophones.** *Here* **means "at" or "in this place."** *Hear* **means "to listen to something." A good way to remember the difference is that** *hear* **has an "ear" in it.**

I am going to put the telephone over **here.**
Can you **hear** it ring?

Another example is *two, to,* **and** *too.* *Two* **is the number between one and three.** *To* **means "toward."** *Too* **means "also" or "more than enough."**

Maggie and Theresa went **to** the movies and ate **two** bags of popcorn. They drank lemonade, **too.**

Show What You Know

Write the correct homophone in each sentence below.

1. "I'm going _____ the tennis court," Meg announced. (too, to, two)

2. Her younger sister, Peg, asked, "May I go, _____?" (too, to, two)

3. Meg said, "Sure, tennis is a game for _____ people." (too, to, two)

4. Meg added, "_____, you may use my old racket." (Here, Hear)

Score: _____   Total Possible: 4

Proofread

Use proper proofreading marks to delete nine incorrect homophones in the story below. Write the correct homophone above each one.

Example: She didn't ~~here~~ _hear_ what you said.

Nick and Alex found an old pirate map and decided <u>two</u> find the buried
₁

treasure. Nick read, "Follow the shoreline <u>two</u> the entrance <u>too</u> the cave."
₂   ₃

The <u>to</u> boys found and entered the cave. "Do you <u>here</u> something?" asked
₄   ₅

Nick.

Alex called <u>to</u> Nick, "I think it's coming from over <u>hear</u>." <u>To</u> furry bats
₆   ₇   ₈

hung from the ceiling above a battered, old chest. Alex took one look at the

bats and said, "I'm out of <u>hear</u>!"
₉

Nick quickly turned and said, "Me <u>two</u>!"
₁₀

Practice

Write two sentences about what the people in the picture might be saying to each other. Use the words _to, too, two, here,_ and _hear._

_____

_____

_____

_____

Tips for Your Own Writing: Proofreading ....

Remember that _two_ is a number for more than one and _too_ is _too_ much, or
more than enough, when you are going _to_ write.

✏️ *This lesson teaches about to/too/two homophones in which you
cannot here/hear a difference in meaning.*

35 Usage: Homophones—Its/It's

When you shorten it is, *you write* it's, *but when* it *owns something, you write* its.

.... **Did You Know?** ....

How to write these two little words, *its* and *it's*, commonly confuses writers.

Its is a word that shows ownership. _Its_ is a personal pronoun that shows possession.

The school lost **its** power during the storm.

_It's_ is a contraction. The apostrophe reminds you that _it's_ stands for the two words _it is_.

It's going to be out for the rest of the day.

Show What You Know

Write *its* or *it's* to correctly complete each sentence below.

1. Listen, _____ the sound of a kitten crying.

2. I hope _____ not lost.

3. The kitten can't find _____ way home.

4. What is _____ name?

5. I don't know because _____ not on _____ collar.

6. Who is _____ owner?

7. Let's look on _____ collar to find out.

8. _____ kind to help a lost animal.

Score: _____   **Total Possible: 9**

Proofread

Use proofreading marks to delete each homophone in bold type that is incorrect. Write the correct word above it. There are four errors.

Example: ~~Its~~ It's time to go home.

The desert can be hot and dry. Some plants have adapted to **it's** climate.
                                                                        1
A cactus has thousands of widespread roots under the ground's surface.

When it rains, **its** roots quickly absorb water. After a rainstorm, **its** possible
                2   3
for a cactus to be filled with water! **It's** thick, tough skin helps to prevent the
                                        4
water from evaporating. A cactus has small, hairy pads on **it's** stem called
                                                            5
areoles. Thorns, flowers, or new branches grow from these.

Practice

Write a paragraph describing a plant that grows where you live. Use *it's* and *its* each at least once.

_____

_____

_____

_____

Tips for Your Own Writing: Proofreading ....

Review a paper you have written describing something. Check to see that if you wrote about ownership, you used *its* and if you used a contraction for *it is*, you wrote *it's.*

If its *shows what is owned, then* it *stands alone—no apostrophe. If* it's *is a contraction, then an apostrophe is part of the action.*

36 Review: Adjectives and Homophones

A. **Write the correct adjective in the blank to complete each sentence.**

1. Daryl is the _____ of the three Robey brothers. (taller, tallest)

2. He is also _____ than his brothers. (more unusual, most unusual)

3. Daryl has _____ hair than both his brothers. (longer, longest)

4. This week it is the _____ shade of purple you can imagine.

(brighter, brightest)

5. Last week, it was an even _____ color. (uglier, ugliest)

6. Daryl has the _____ hair of anyone I know. (stranger, strangest)

7. He's also the _____ guy in the world! (friendlier, friendliest)

Score: _____   Total Possible: 7

B. **The paragraph below has six mistakes in adjectives that compare. Use proofreading marks to delete each incorrect adjective and write the correct one above it.**

Alaskan brown bears and grizzly bears are the larger bears in the world. They are easily angered but usually will not attack unless they are threatened. The American black bear is the most commonest species. These bears are fast runners and agile climbers. Asiatic black bears are smallest than American black bears. They are also fiercest than most other kinds of bears. Sun bears are the most small kind of bear. Their claws are more curved and have sharpest points than those of any other kind of bear. Bears spend the day sleeping and the night hunting for food.

Score: _____   Total Possible: 6

C. Write the correct homophone to complete each sentence.

1. Dad said I could invite _____ friends to the ball game. (to, too, two)

2. I asked Jonah and Julie _____ come with us. (to, too, two)

3. We all wanted to _____ the announcer sing. (hear, here)

4. He always sings, "Take Me Out _____ the Ball Game." (to, too, two)

5. Driving to the game, traffic was backed up _____ miles. (to, too, two)

6. Finally, Dad reached a parking lot and said, "We'll park _____." (hear, here)

7. Many other cars pulled into the lot, _____. (to, too, two)

Score: _____   Total Possible: 7

D. Write *its* or *it's* on each line to complete the sentences below.

What swims slowly through the warm tropical water? _____ head is

like a horse's and _____ tail is like a monkey's. _____ a sea horse! It
                         2   3

carries _____ baby sea horses in a pouch until they're ready to be born.
        4

But _____ not the mother that carries the babies. _____ the father! A
    5   6

father sea horse carries hundreds of babies in _____ pouch. Baby sea
                                                7

horses can look after themselves as soon as they are born.

Score: _____   Total Possible: 7

REVIEW SCORE: _____   REVIEW TOTAL: 27

37 Usage: Regular Plurals

*T*here are plural (more than one) ways to make a word plural!

A noun that stands for one person, place, or thing is *singular*.

The clown sharpened the huge **pencil**.

A noun that stands for more than one person, place, or thing is *plural*.

The clown sharpened four huge **pencils**.

Add -*s* to the ends of most nouns to form the plural.

Add -*es* to nouns ending in *ss*, *x*, *ch*, or *sh*.

class—class**es**   peach—peach**es**
brush—brush**es**   box—box**es**

Change the *y* to *i* and add -*es* to nouns that end in a consonant and *y*.

sky—sk**ies**   story—stor**ies**

Show What You Know

Write a plural noun above for each singular noun that is underlined.

The <u>beach</u> on this island are sandy. Sometimes the <u>wave</u> crash against
    1   2

the pier. Many <u>family</u> come here to play in the sun. My family comes here on
              3

<u>Sunday</u> during the summer. Terri likes to search for <u>shell</u>. She has <u>box</u> filled
4   5   6

with them. Angela builds <u>sand castle</u>. Dad spends his whole time taking
                           7

<u>photo</u> of us.
8

Score: _____   Total Possible: 8

Proofread

There are six incorrect plurals in the paragraph below. Use proofreading marks to delete each underlined word that is incorrect and write the correct plural above it.

Example: He is listening to <u>storys</u> on the radio. *stories*

Jeremy has two <u>gardenes</u> in his yard. In one garden, he grows <u>petuniaes</u>

               1   **2**

and <u>daisies</u>. In the other, he grows <u>carrotes</u> and <u>beanes</u>. There are raspberry

   3   **4**   **5**

<u>bushs</u> along the edge of the garden. Yesterday, Jeremy picked <u>bunchs</u> of

6   **7**

fresh, green spinach for dinner.

Practice

Write a paragraph describing what is happening in the picture. Use plural nouns.

_____

_____

_____

_____

_____

_____

Tips for Your Own Writing: Proofreading ·······················

When you write plural forms, be sure to add *-es* to words that end in *sh, ch, s, ss,* and *x,* and always change the *y* to *i* before you add *-es* to make words that end in *y* plural.

With these simple rules, you don't have to rely on hunches to make most words plural.

38 Usage: Irregular Plurals

Just when you think you know all the rules about making plurals, you'll find there are words that don't follow the rules.

.... **Did You Know?** ....

There are some nouns that do not follow the rules for most plural nouns.

Some nouns have irregular plural forms. These plural nouns do not follow a pattern, so you just have to memorize them.

woman—women	man—men	child—children
foot—feet	goose—geese	ox—oxen
mouse—mice	tooth—teeth	cactus—cacti

For some nouns, the singular and plural forms are the same.

deer—deer	moose—moose	trout—trout
sheep—sheep	series—series	corps—corps

Show What You Know

Read the following sentences. Write the singular form above each underlined word.

Dad and Uncle Glen are taking a <u>series</u> of fishing classes. They want to
                                    1

learn how to catch <u>salmon</u>. Last month they went on a fishing trip with
                     2

several other <u>men</u>. Uncle Glen caught five <u>trout</u>. His <u>feet</u> were cold from
              3   4   5

standing in the stream for hours. Dad didn't catch anything but two <u>mice</u> in
                                                                     6

his tent!

Score: _____   Total Possible: 6

Proofread

There are four incorrect plurals in the paragraph below. Use proofreading marks to delete each underlined word that is incorrect and write the correct plural above it.

Example: Mary lost two ~~tooths~~ ^teeth last night.

Mom invited four <u>womans</u> out to the farm for a picnic. Each one brought
₁

her <u>childs</u>. One child wanted to feed the <u>sheep</u>. Another wanted to pet the
₂ ₃

<u>gooses</u>. The littlest child dangled his <u>foots</u> in the pond.
₄ ₅

Practice

Write a paragraph that tells about the picture. Use the plural forms of nouns when you can.

_____

_____

_____

_____

_____

Tips for Your Own Writing: Proofreading ....

Sometimes when you write a plural, the word you write does not look right. Keep a dictionary handy to check the spelling of the plural form. Dictionaries show the singular form in bold type and then show the plurals if they are irregular.

Don't get cold feet/foots about forming irregular plurals.

39 Usage: Singular Possessives

Singular nouns take apostrophe s when they show that the noun has or owns something.

.... **Did You Know?** ....

**A possessive noun shows ownership or a relationship between two things. An apostrophe (')
is always used to mark possessive nouns.**

> Jane**'s** mountain bike is red.
> The windowsill is the cat**'s** favorite place to sleep.

A singular possessive noun shows ownership by one person or thing.

> Gary**'s** locker   the principal**'s** office

To make a singular noun possessive, just add 's.
> the smile of the baby—the baby**'s** smile

Show What You Know

On each line below, write the possessive form of the word in parentheses.

1. This is the house that Jack built. Is this _____ house? (Jack)

2. Mary has a garden. How does _____ garden grow? (Mary)

3. Little Boy Blue, come blow your horn. The _____ flute broke. (girl)

4. Jack jumped over the candlestick. Did the _____ flame hurt? (candle)

5. A wise old owl lived in an oak. Is the tree really the _____ home? (owl)

6. Little Miss Muffet sat on a tuffet. Where was the _____ chair? (girl)

Score: _____   Total Possible: 6

Proofread

Read the paragraph below. There are three apostrophes missing. Use the proper proofreading marks to add an apostrophe to words that show possession.

Example: We are going to Alisha's house after school.

Dad can't find his car keys. He thinks he may have left them in Grandpas truck. I think he dropped them near Grandmas rosebushes. He has another set of keys, but they are in his boss's car. I said, "Let's look in Moms purse. You can find anything in there!"

Practice

The animals are having a garage sale to raise money for a new park. Write a paragraph about what each animal has brought to sell. Use singular possessive nouns when you can.

_____

_____

_____

_____

_____

Tips for Your Own Writing: Proofreading ....

Do not confuse plurals and possessives that sound alike, like _Dads_ and _Dad's_. Remember the apostrophe s to make the possessive.

When a singular noun is possessive, add a simple 's to it.

40 Usage: Singular and Plural Possessives

Possessives help you hold your own.

.... **Did You Know?** ....

A singular possessive noun shows ownership by one person or thing.

the **ship's** captain   the **sailor's** uniform

A plural possessive noun shows ownership by more than one person or thing.

the **cities'** streets   the **states'** governors

To make a plural noun that ends in *s* a possessive noun, add only the apostrophe.

girls—girls'   schools—schools'

To make a plural noun that does not end in *s* a possessive noun, add an apostrophe and *s*.

children—children**'s**   teeth—teeth**'s**

Show What You Know

Change the underlined words to include a plural possessive noun. The first one is done for you.

1. The cameras show the <u>faces of the sea otters</u>.
   sea otters' faces

2. Otters sometimes play by sliding down the <u>slopes of the riverbanks</u>.

3. The <u>mother of pups</u> watches them as they play.

4. The mother otter cracks open the <u>shells of sea urchins</u> for food.

5. She grooms the <u>coats of the babies</u> to keep them clean and waterproof.

Score: _____   Total Possible: 4

Proofread

Read the paragraph below. There are four apostrophes and one apostrophe *s* missing. Use proper proofreading marks to show where they should be added.

Example: The men᭄s tennis match is tomorrow.

During the monthly teachers meeting, Principal Clark announced that the district would hold an all schools' camp out on May 24. Highview school was going to pitch tents in the park. Well, this idea certainly grabbed the students attention! The boys campsite would be out near the playground, and the girls area would be next to the tennis courts. There would be more than 400 kids in the park. Some of the children parents would be there, too!

Practice

Write a paragraph to describe what is happening in the picture. Use both singular and plural possessive nouns.

_____

_____

_____

_____

_____

Tips for Your Own Writing: Proofreading ....

When you write plural possessives, you usually add only an apostrophe unless you have a plural that does not end in *s*, and then you add an apostrophe *s*.

Children's, *not* childrens', *is the correct plural possessive.*

41 Usage: Plurals and Possessives

Is it a plural or a possessive? Let the apostrophe be your guide.

·· **Did You Know?** ····························

People are sometimes confused by possessives and plurals because the two forms sound alike, but they are written differently. The possessive form always has an apostrophe. The apostrophe is the signal that means ownership.

Jeremy collects old *coins.* (plural)
Jeremy's collection was at the library. (singular possessive)
The *coins'* value increases every year. (plural possessive)

··

Show What You Know

Read each sentence. If the underlined word means more than one, write *plural* on the line. If it shows ownership, write *possessive*.

1. <u>Millions</u> visit the Grand Canyon yearly. _____

2. Most of them view the canyon from one of the <u>rims</u>. _____

3. The <u>canyon's</u> walls show layers of rock. _____

4. The <u>earth's</u> forces and erosion formed the Grand Canyon. _____

5. Guides can answer <u>hikers'</u> questions. _____

6. The <u>Colorado River's</u> rapids provide exciting raft trips. _____

7. There are many different <u>trails</u> inside the canyon. _____

8. Beautiful, clear-blue <u>waterfalls</u> roar down the sides of the canyon. _____

Score: _____   Total Possible: 8

Proofread

Use proofreading marks to delete three mistakes in plural and possessive forms in the note below. Write the correct word above each mistake.

Example: The ~~runner's~~ runners are in place.

> Dear Mr. Cirrillo,
>
> Ted and I really enjoyed going to the rodeo. I liked the
>
> bucking broncos' best. The riders skills were awesome. Ted
>
> liked the rodeo clowns. Thanks for one of summers great
>
> memories!
>
> Sincerely,
>
> Brian West

Practice

Write a paragraph describing the animals in the picture. Use both plural and possessive nouns.

_____

_____

_____

_____

_____

Tips for Your Own Writing: Proofreading ....

If you are not sure whether a word is a plural or a possessive, look to see if a noun comes right after the word. If it does, the word is probably possessive.

 A *possessive noun must own something.*

42 Usage: Contractions with *Not*

✏️*A* contraction is one word that was once two. When you make a contraction, you squeeze together (or contract) the two words into one.

.... **Did You Know?** ....

A contraction is a shortened form of two words that are joined together. When the words are contracted, some letters are left out. An apostrophe takes the place of the letters that have been left out.

My bicycle **does not** work.   My bicycle **doesn't** work.

Many contractions are made by putting together a verb and the word *not*.

did not—did**n't**	are not—are**n't**
do not—do**n't**	was not—was**n't**
have not—have**n't**	could not—could**n't**
has not—has**n't**	should not—should**n't**

Two exceptions are:

cannot—ca**n't**   will not—wo**n't**

··

Show What You Know

Write a contraction above the underlined words in each sentence.

We <u>are not</u> smiling. The car <u>will not</u> start, and the mechanic <u>cannot</u> fix it
   1   2   3

until Friday. Antonia <u>could not</u> go to her piano lesson. Raphael <u>was not</u> able
                      4   5

to go to baseball practice. I <u>have not</u> gone to the library to work on my
                              6

report. We probably <u>should not</u> blame "Old Betsy."
                    7

Score: _____   Total Possible: 7

Proofread

The are five mistakes in contractions in the note below. Use the proper proofreading marks to add apostrophes where they are needed.

Example: They haven't come outside yet.

> Dear Teresa,
>
> I wont be home from work until 7:30 tonight. Dad cant make it home early either. Carlito doesnt have a soccer game today, so he will be home at about 4:00. Why dont you finish your homework together? I didnt plan anything for dinner, so we will order pizza when I get home.
>
> Love,
>
> *Mom*

Practice

On another piece of paper, write a letter to a company telling them what you think about one of their products. Describe what you like and dislike about the product.

Tips for Your Own Writing: Proofreading ....

Contractions are like shortcuts. You cannot take the shortcut without using an apostrophe. Check your contractions.

Won't *is a special contraction. It is formed from the words* will *and* not *but is not* "willn't."

43 Usage: Contractions with *Am, Have, Will, Is,* and *Are*

Contractions are a kind of shorthand. Two words are shortened into one.

.... **Did You Know?** ....

Some contractions are formed by joining the words *I, you, she, he, it, we,* or *they* with a verb.

I + am = I'm

I + have = I've

he + is = he's

she + is = she's

it + is = it's

she + will = she'll

we + are = we're

we + have = we've

you + are = you're

they + are = they're

they + will = they'll

Show What You Know

Write the letter of the words in Column B that matches the contraction in Column A.

Column A	Column B
_____ **1.** I'm	**a.** you are
_____ **2.** they're	**b.** I have
_____ **3.** you're	**c.** we are
_____ **4.** I've	**d.** it is
_____ **5.** we're	**e.** they are
_____ **6.** it's	**f.** she will
_____ **7.** she'll	**g.** I am

Score: _____   **Total Possible: 7**

Proofread

Read the following paragraph. Use proofreading marks to delete four incorrect contractions and write the correct contraction above each one.

Example: My sister thinks ~~shes~~ she's going to the ball game.

    Wev'e got tickets to the ice show. You'll be amazed at how the skaters seem to fly over the ice. Ive never seen professional skaters before. My brother plays hockey and he'is a great fan of all ice sports. He'll really appreciate the skaters' skills. He thinks theyll combine both power and style!

Practice

Read about an athlete or another person you admire. Write a paragraph telling about why you admire the person. Use contractions to make your writing sound more natural.

_____

_____

_____

_____

_____

Tips for Your Own Writing: Proofreading ....

If you are not sure about where to place the apostrophe, think about the two words that the contraction replaces. Then make sure you place the apostrophe where the letters are missing.

It's a fact! You need an apostrophe when words contract.

44 Review: Plurals, Possessives, Contractions

A. Write the plural form of each word on the lines below.

1. journey _____

2. brush _____

3. box _____

4. puppy _____

5. baby _____

6. surprise _____

7. beach _____

8. glass _____

Score: _____ Total Possible: 8

B. Write the plural form of each word on the lines below.

1. woman _____

2. tooth _____

3. man _____

4. goose _____

5. mouse _____

6. deer _____

7. child _____

8. moose _____

Score: _____ Total Possible: 8

C. Add an apostrophe to four boldfaced words that show ownership.

A tornado swept through the **streets** of the city last night. A **buildings**
                                    1   2
roof was peeled away. The big oak **trees** leaves were pulled from its
                                          3
branches. Many **cars** were turned over. The **citys** water supply was cut off.
                      4   5
Some **roads** were closed. The **librarys** windows were shattered.
          6   7

Score: _____ Total Possible: 4

D. Rewrite each of the following phrases on the lines, using a plural possessive.

1. the names of the countries   _____

2. the products of the regions   _____

3. the crops of the farmers   _____

4. the jobs of the workers   _____

Score: _____   Total Possible: 4

E. Circle the correct form of the word in each sentence below.

The (teams, teams') were ready to race. Each (schools, school's) team

          1   2
wore a different color. The (runners, runner's) began to line up. Where were

                    3
(Rosas, Rosa's) shoes? (Whistles, Whistle's) began to blow!

  4   5

Score: _____   Total Possible: 5

F. Read each sentence below. Write the two words that make up each of the four underlined contractions on the lines.

1. Some people <u>don't</u> follow basic safety rules.   _____

2. Children <u>shouldn't</u> play on busy streets.   _____

3. Jim <u>didn't</u> look both ways before crossing the highway.   _____

4. Aaron <u>wasn't</u> wearing his seat belt.   _____

Score: _____   Total Possible: 4

G. Write the contraction for the underlined words above each.

<u>I have</u> invited ten classmates to a pizza party. <u>We will</u> order pizza. <u>We are</u>

  1   2   3
going to eat outside. <u>It is</u> nice to finally have warm weather.

                        4

Score: _____   Total Possible: 4

REVIEW SCORE: _____   REVIEW TOTAL: 37

45 Usage: Regular Verb Tense

Verbs change to show the past because today becomes yesterday so fast.

.... **Did You Know?** ....

Tense is a word that means "time." The tense of a verb tells you when the action takes place.

A verb in the *present tense* shows action that happens now.

The soccer players **kick** the ball toward the net.

A verb in the *past tense* shows action that already happened. Add *-ed* to form the past tense of most verbs.

The soccer players **kicked** the ball toward the net.

To form the past tense of verbs that end in *e*, drop the *e* and add *-ed*.

rake—rak**ed**   place—plac**ed**   taste—tast**ed**

Show What You Know

Write the past tense of the verb in parentheses.

1. We _____ to the movies. (walk)

2. We didn't know that Len's dog _____ us. (follow)

3. We didn't notice that people _____ at us. (point)

4. We finally _____ around. (turn)

5. Skipper _____ a dollar bill in his mouth. (carry)

Score: _____   Total Possible: 5

Proofread

There are four mistakes in verb tense in the paragraph below. Use proper proofreading marks to add *-ed* to show action that has already happened. In one mistake, you must drop an *e* before you add the *-ed*.

Example: He taste‸ lobster for the first time yesterday.
        (ed)

    In 1497, Amerigo Vespucci sail to a new land. He call it *Mundus Novus,* which means "New World" in Latin. Many years later, a German geographer decide to name the new land *America* after Amerigo Vespucci. The new land was South America. Later, North America, where Viking explorers first land in about A.D. 1000, was also named after Amerigo Vespucci.

Practice

Write a paragraph about an explorer you know about. When you are finished writing, reread your paragraph to check for the proper spelling of past tense verbs.

_____

_____

_____

_____

_____

Tips for Your Own Writing: Proofreading ....

Make sure that if you write about something that has already happened you use the past tense of the verbs.

 Don't let verbs make you tense!

46 Usage: Irregular Verb Tense

Irregular verbs break the rules!

.... Did You Know? ....

Some verbs are special. They do not end in *-ed* to show past time. These verbs are called *irregular verbs* because they do not follow the pattern for forming the past tense. They have one special spelling to show past time.

Erica **takes** us to the city each month. (present)
Last month, she **took** us to the art museum. (past)
We usually **ride** the train to the city. (present)
On our last trip, we **rode** the bus. (past)

Other irregular verbs include:

break—broke	begin—began	come—came
do—did	draw—drew	eat—ate
make—made	think—thought	write—wrote
say—said	catch—caught	run—ran
grow—grew	win—won	give—gave

Show What You Know

Write the past tense of the verb that correctly completes each sentence over each underlined irregular verb.

Julio <u>run</u> in a 5K race last week. He <u>think</u> that he would win. Tanya <u>come</u>
   1   2   3

from behind and <u>catch</u> up with Julio. Tanya passed him and <u>win</u> the race. She
                4   5

<u>break</u> the school record. Julio <u>do</u> not feel bad about losing the race. He <u>say</u> he
 6   7   8

will try harder next time.

Score: _____   Total Possible: 8

Proofread

Read the paragraph below. Use proofreading marks to delete six incorrect verbs in the sentences and write the correct verb above each one.

Example: Todd ~~catch~~ the biggest fish.
                     caught

Last year, Samantha grow pumpkins in the garden. She give one to Linda.

Linda take the pumpkin home. She drew a face on the pumpkin. Her mom

make a pumpkin pie. Linda eat the seeds. Then she write Samantha a thank-

you note.

Practice

You have a green thumb and your vegetables are huge! Write a paragraph about your garden. Use the past tense of _grow, give, spring, begin,_ and _buy._

_____

_____

_____

_____

_____

_____

Tips for Your Own Writing: Proofreading ....

Saying the past tense aloud can help you decide whether the verb takes _-ed_ to form the past tense or is irregular. _Sitted_ just does not sound right!

If you are not sure about the past tense of a verb, look it up in a dictionary.

47 Usage: Verb Agreement

Do you ever wear a winter coat and a bathing suit together? Parts of a sentence have to "go together" just as your clothes do.

.... **Did You Know?** ....

The verb has to agree with the subject of the sentence. This means that they must both be either singular or plural.

Usually if the subject is singular, or the pronoun *he, she,* or *it,* add -*s* or -*es* to the verb.

> Dad **remembers** when few homes had TV sets.
> He often **reads** to the class.

If the subject is more than one, or the pronoun *I, you, we,* or *they,* do <u>not</u> add -*s* or -*es* to the verb.

> My parents always **watch** the news on TV.
> I **ride** my bike to school.

Show What You Know

Write the verb on the line that correctly completes each sentence.

1. Adam _____ on the new computer. (works, work)

2. He _____ it to do his homework. (use, uses)

3. His brothers _____ games on it. (plays, play)

4. His mom _____ stories on it. (writes, write)

5. His sister _____ reports for school. (type, types)

6. They _____ many jobs easier. (makes, make)

Score: _____   **Total Possible: 6**

Proofread

Read the paragraph below. There are five mistakes in subject/verb agreement. Use proofreading marks to delete each incorrect word and write the correct word above it.

Example: Jessica ~~talk~~ talks on the phone too long.

The birth of a baby elephant at the zoo is an exciting event. Soon after it is born, the baby wobble to its feet. Its mother nudge it to take its first steps. The thirsty baby drink its mother's milk. The older elephants stroke it with their trunks to welcome it to the herd. Mama elephant teach it to use its trunk to drink and grab food. She even show it how to squirt showers of water over itself.

Practice

Add verbs to sentences 1 and 3. Add subjects to sentences 2 and 4. Make sure each subject and verb work together.

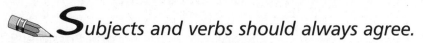

1. Mountain hikers _____ .

2. _____ appears in the distance.

3. A family of bears _____ .

4. _____ block the trail.

Tips for Your Own Writing: Proofreading ....

Let your ears be the judge of whether the parts of the sentence agree with each other. Read what you write out loud.

Subjects and verbs should always agree.

Lesson

48 Review: Verbs

A. Each sentence shows present time. Use proofreading marks to change the eight underlined verbs to show past time. Write the past tense of the verb above each underlined word.

Officer Jane <u>comes</u> to speak to our class. She <u>brings</u> safety posters. She
       1   **2**

<u>talks</u> about bicycle and playground safety. She <u>helps</u> us write some safety
3   **4**

rules of our own. Our teacher <u>shows</u> us a film about school bus safety.
                                   5

Then we <u>tour</u> the police station. We <u>ask</u> Captain Jarvis about traffic safety. He
        6   **7**

<u>offers</u> us a ride in his police car.
8

                                  Score: _____   Total Possible: 8

B. Write the correct verb to complete each sentence.

1. Astronauts often _____ up in space today. (go, went)

2. Some people once _____ space travel was impossible. (think, thought)

3. In the 1960s, Neil Armstrong _____ in *Apollo II.* (fly, flew)

4. He actually _____ on the surface of the moon. (stand, stood)

5. He _____ moon rocks back to Earth. (bring, brought)

6. Reporters _____ many stories about the lunar landing. (write, wrote)

7. Millions of Americans _____ the moon landing on TV. (see, saw)

8. Today astronauts no longer _____ to the moon. (fly, flew)

9. Now they _____ the space shuttle to and from space. (take, took)

                                  Score: _____   Total Possible: 9

C. Write the past tense of each verb on the line.

1. The itsy-bitsy spider climb up the water spout. _____

2. Down come the rain. _____

3. It wash the spider out. _____

4. Out come the sun. _____

5. It dry up all the rain. _____

6. The itsy-bitsy spider crawl up the spout again. _____

Score: _____   Total Possible: 6

D. Write the correct form of the word in parentheses to complete each sentence.

1. The bus _____ late this morning. (is, are)

2. We _____ at the corner. (wait, waits)

3. Dad _____ to drive us to school. (offers, offer)

4. The traffic signal _____ on the highway. (breaks, break)

5. We _____ the bus at the last minute. (boards, board)

6. Our teacher, Ms. Kerr, _____ outside. (waits, wait)

Score: _____   Total Possible: 6

E. Write a present tense verb that agrees with each subject.

1. (to buy)   She _____   **4.** (to wear) He _____

2. (to see)   I _____   **5.** (to carry) They _____

3. (to cry)   Bill _____   **6.** (to lean) It _____

Score: _____   Total Possible: 6

REVIEW SCORE: _____   REVIEW TOTAL: 35

49 Usage: Subject Pronoun Agreement

✏️ *What do pronouns replace? They replace nouns or other pronouns.*

·················· **Did You Know?** ··················

A pronoun is a word that can take the place of one or more nouns or pronouns in a sentence.

> Franklin was a printer. **He** was also a writer.

Subject pronouns are used as subjects in a sentence. Subjects are the persons or things that do whatever is being done in the sentence.

I, you, he, she, **and** *it* **are subject pronouns that mean only one.**

> **I** saw Henri. **He** was with Sam.

You, we, **and** *they* **are subject pronouns that mean more than one.**

> Jill and I are friends. **We** are close.

When you use *I* **with another noun or pronoun, you should put** *I* **last.**

> Liu and **I** went to the library.

Show What You Know

Read each sentence below. Circle the five subject pronouns.

What do you know about Sally Ride? She was the first female astronaut in the U.S. space program. In 1983 Sally rocketed into space on a space shuttle. It was named *Challenger*. She and John Fabian operated the shuttle's robotic arm. They used it to launch and retrieve satellites.

Score: _____   Total Possible: 5

Proofread

On the line, write a pronoun to take the place of the underlined word or words in each sentence.

Example: <u>John</u> worked on the committee, and ___he___ also decorated.

    <u>Kyle and Karen</u> wanted to earn money because ___1___ wanted to go to summer camp. <u>Kyle</u> made flyers, and ___2___ gave the flyers to all the neighbors. <u>The flyers</u> read "Lawn Mowing, $6 each yard," and ___3___ listed Kyle's phone number. <u>Mr. Karres, Ms. Blumberg, and I</u> called the number on the flyers, and ___4___ asked Kyle to mow our lawns. Later, I saw the <u>flyer</u> Karen made, and ___5___ read "Dogs walked twice a day for $10 a week." I called <u>Karen</u> in the morning, and ___6___ came to meet my dog. Now <u>Karen and Kyle</u> both work for me, and ___7___ do an excellent job.

Practice

Talk with your friends about a way you can earn money next summer. Then on another piece of paper, write a flyer to describe your services and fees. Use subject pronouns when you can.

Tips for Your Own Writing: Revising

Do you want to avoid repeating a subject noun over and over again in your writing? If so, replace the noun with a subject pronoun. Remember to let your reader know what the pronoun refers to.

✏️ *U*se a pronoun *correctly by making it clear what* it *replaces.*

50 Usage: Object Pronoun Agreement

*P*ronouns are good stand-ins for nouns. Learn when and how to use pronouns to get the job done!

.... **Did You Know?** ....

A pronoun is a word that can take the place of one or more nouns or other pronouns in a sentence.

> Carl gave the ball to Lou, and Lou dropped the **ball.**
> Carl gave the ball to Lou, and Lou dropped **it.**

Object pronouns follow action verbs and words like *to, for, at, of,* and *with. Me, you, him, her,* and *it* are used when you are writing about a singular object.

> Hector gave **me** a piñata from Mexico.
> Did Hector buy one for **you?**

***Us, you,* and *them* are used when you are talking about a plural object.**

> Mai called Jim and me to ask **us** to the movies.
> We always have a good time with **them.**

....

Show What You Know

Write the correct pronoun in each blank.

1. Jeff was teaching Rita and ـــــ how to play tennis. (I, me)

2. He showed ـــــ over and over again how to hold our rackets. (we, us)

3. Rita said it was too awkward for ـــــ. (she, her)

4. Hitting the ball was a problem for ـــــ. (me, I)

5. I spent a lot of time chasing after ـــــ! (them, they)

Score: ـــــ   Total Possible: 5

Proofread

There are five mistakes in the use of object pronouns in the paragraph below. Use proofreading marks to delete each incorrect pronoun and write the correct pronoun above it.

Example: Jessica couldn't find ~~he~~. _{him}

Dad read nursery rhymes to my sister and I when we were young. Each of we had a favorite rhyme. My sister liked "Jack and Jill." Dad must have read it to her 1,000 times! I also liked it, but my favorite one was "Three Little Kittens." That rhyme is about kittens who lost their mittens and couldn't find they. I don't ask Dad to read to I anymore. Now I ask if I can read to he.

Practice

Write a paragraph about something you do with someone in your family. As you write, use object pronouns to avoid repeating the same noun.

_____

_____

_____

_____

_____

Tips for Your Own Writing: Proofreading ....

Remember that object pronouns follow action verbs and words like *to* and *of*. Check that the pronouns you use as objects are *me, it, him, her, us, you,* and *them.*

Object pronouns can be used in place of nouns used as objects.

51 Usage: Double Negatives

Should you ever use double negatives? No, not never!

.... **Did You Know?** ....

Sometimes when you write a sentence, you use a negative word like *no*. *None*, *nothing*, *never*, and *no one* are also negative words.

> Rob will **never** weed the garden.
> **None** of the yard work was finished.

The word *not* and contractions made with *not* are also negatives.

> I did **not** water the plants.   He **won't** rake the leaves.

Only one negative word is needed in a sentence.

There are two ways to correct a double negative. A positive word can replace a negative word, or the *n't* can be dropped.

> **Incorrect:** There **weren't no** books on the shelf.
> **Correct:** There **weren't any** books on the shelf *or*
> there **were no** books on the shelf.

....

Show What You Know

Complete each sentence by writing the correct word in the blank.

1. Most people _____ never get caught in a fire. (will, won't)

2. Never store _____ paint in open cans. (no, any)

3. Don't _____ use gasoline to start a bonfire or grill. (never, ever)

4. Never leave ____ candle or fire unattended. (a, no)

Score: _____   Total Possible: 4

Proofread

There are four double negatives in the note below. Use proofreading marks to delete the double negatives and write the corrections above them.

Example: Sarah ~~doesn't never~~ ^{doesn't ever} want to go there again.

Dear Hugh,

I won't never pick flowers in the woods again. There wasn't no warning sign. How was I to know what poison ivy looked like? No one never told me about it. There isn't any way to get rid of it. Nothing won't stop the itching!

Your rash-covered friend,

Matt

Practice

Make up a list of classroom rules. Write sentences using the words *no*, *never*, *nothing*, or *none* or sentences with negative contractions.

_____

_____

_____

_____

Tips for Your Own Writing: Proofreading ....

You always want to avoid having two negatives in one sentence. When you check your writing, if there is more than one, get rid of one.

Never, no never say, "I don't have no homework!"

Lesson
52 Review: Pronouns and Double Negatives

A. On each blank, write a subject pronoun that could refer to the underlined words.

Christine and I are in the same Explorer Troop, and _____ went on a
1
rafting trip together. Christine asked me if _____ was afraid. This was
2
Christine's first rafting trip, and _____ was a little bit frightened. The
3
guides said that _____ always followed the safety rules and would watch
4
us carefully. The guides were right about the trip down the river. _____
5
was very exciting, and no one got hurt.

Score: _____   Total Possible: 5

B. On each blank, write an object pronoun that refers to the underlined word(s).

Dad asked if my sister and I wanted to go to work with _____. Ariella
1
and I jumped at the chance to see the factory, and so on Friday Dad took
_____ there. As we walked through the assembly line, Dad explained how
2
_____ worked. I watched Dad work on the line, and he showed _____
3   4
how to use a drill to tighten bolts. Just then a whistle blew. All the workers
grabbed their lunches, and we followed _____ to the lunchroom. We ate
5
lunch and then Dad took us home. Ariella and I had a great time at the
factory, and we hope Dad will take _____ there again.
6

Score: _____   Total Possible: 6

C. **Write the eleven correct pronouns in the following paragraphs.**

One of the three little pigs said to the others, "_____ need to build new
$\quad$ **1** (We, Us)

houses." Each of _____ built a new house. _____ used different
$\qquad$ **2** (they, them) $\qquad\qquad$ **3** (They, Them)

materials to build their houses. Millie Pig told them not to use straw or sticks

to build their houses, but two of _____ didn't listen to _____.
$\qquad\qquad$ **4** (they, them) $\qquad\qquad$ **5** (she, her)

When the wolf came, _____ easily blew down the houses that had
$\qquad$ **6** (he, him)

been built of straw and sticks. Then the wolf went to the one brick house and

said, "Open up, or _____ will blow your house down." Of course, _____
$\qquad$ **7** (I, me) $\qquad\qquad$ **8** (he, him)

couldn't blow it down, and so the wolf slid down the chimney. The pig had a

surprise for _____, though. _____ landed in a pot of boiling water. That
$\qquad$ **9** (he, him) $\qquad$ **10** (He, Him)

old wolf jumped out of the pot and ran away. _____ never bothered the
$\qquad\qquad$ **11** (He, Him)

pigs again.

$\qquad\qquad\qquad$ **Score:** _____ $\qquad$ **Total Possible: 11**

D. **Read the paragraph below. Use proper proofreading marks to delete
five incorrect bold words and write the correct word above each one.**

I don't really **never** like to clean my room. Cleaning isn't **nothing** I would
$\qquad$ **1** $\qquad\qquad\qquad\qquad\qquad\qquad$ **2**

choose to do. Dad said that I didn't have **no** choice. I had to clean my room,
$\qquad\qquad\qquad\qquad\qquad\qquad$ **3**

or I couldn't invite anyone over to the house. He said that I could have

anyone over to see this mess. Yes, I cleaned my room, and I promised that I
4

wouldn't **never** leave it in such a mess again.
5

$\qquad\qquad\qquad\qquad$ **Score:** _____ $\qquad$ **Total Possible: 5**

$\qquad\qquad\qquad$ **REVIEW SCORE:** _____ $\qquad$ **REVIEW TOTAL: 27**

53 Grammar: Nouns

Imagine a circus in your mind. Can you see the clowns, tigers, and tightrope walkers? Do you smell the popcorn and cotton candy? Nouns are words that make pictures in the reader's mind.

.... Did You Know? ....

A *noun* is a word that tells who or what did the action or was acted upon in the sentence.

The **ringmaster** wore a tall, shiny, black **hat.**

A *common noun* names any person or place.

woman   mountain   school

A *singular noun* names one person, place, or thing and a *plural noun* names more than one.

singular—town   plural—towns

A *proper noun* names a particular person or place. Proper nouns start with capital letters.

Eleanor Roosevelt   Southside School

A *possessive noun* names who or what owns something.

Pedro's basketball   the dog's bone   the actor's role

Show What You Know

Circle the common nouns in the following paragraph. Underline the proper nouns.

Dodoes once lived on the island of Mauritius in the Indian Ocean. Dodoes

were very unusual birds. Their wings were very tiny, and so dodoes could not

fly. A dodo was as big as a large turkey. These birds no longer exist.

Score: _____   Total Possible: 11

Practice

Replace the underlined common noun in each sentence with a proper noun. Write the proper noun above the common noun.

Example: Some students in <u>the school</u> are
Lincoln Elementary School
interested in astronomy.

<u>Two girls</u> from our class went on a trip to
1
the planetarium. The planetarium was in <u>the city</u>.
2
<u>One girl</u> asked a question about <u>a planet</u>.
3 **4**
<u>The other girl</u> was reading a book. It was
5
about <u>an astronaut</u>. The astronaut flew on
6
<u>the space shuttle</u>. Returning from space, the shuttle landed in <u>a state</u>.
7 **8**
The astronaut met <u>the President</u>.
9

Revise

Write another noun above each underlined noun to make the paragraph more interesting. Share your sentences with your classmates.

Have you ever visited a pet <u>place</u>? If you have, then you know there are
1
many kinds of <u>things</u> for sale there. In the window, you might see some frisky
2
<u>animals</u>. In hanging cages, you might notice some colorful <u>birds</u>. No doubt
3 **4**
you would see <u>containers</u> filled with <u>animals</u>. In smaller cages, you might see
5 **6**
some <u>animals</u> running around on a wheel.
7

Tips for Your Own Writing: Revising ....

Choose a piece of your own writing. Underline the nouns. Check that you used the best noun in each position. Using a specific common noun or proper nouns can add information and color to your sentences.

The name's the thing! Choosing the best noun for the job will make your writing more interesting.

111

54 Grammar: Pronouns

What did the pronoun say to the noun? Anything you can do I can do, too!

Did You Know?

A *pronoun* is a word that takes the place of a noun or nouns. They help you avoid using the same nouns over and over. Pronouns change their spelling according to their use.

John said that **John** was going to ride **John's** bike.

John said that **he** was going to ride **his** bike.

***I, you, she,* and *they* are examples of <u>subject pronouns</u>.**

Squanto was a member of the Pawtuxet tribe.

He was a member of the Pawtuxet tribe.

***Me, him, us,* and *them* are examples of <u>object pronouns</u>.**

Squanto showed the **colonists** how to fish.

Squanto showed **them** how to fish.

***My, your,* and *their* are examples of <u>possessive pronouns</u>.**

Squanto's friendship was important.

His friendship was important.

Show What You Know

Circle the pronouns in the sentences below.

Have you ever heard of Jane Addams? She wanted to help people living in poverty. There were no government agencies to help them. Addams established a settlement house in Chicago. It was a place to receive help and learn new skills. The settlement house helped many people and made their lives easier.

Score: _____   Total Possible: 5

Practice

Write a pronoun in each of the blanks so that the paragraph makes sense.

Four little ducklings pecked _____ way out of _____ eggs. Mother
                                           1   2

Duck watched excitedly as _____ babies climbed out of the shells. When
                                             3

the time came, Mother Duck waddled out of _____
                                                        4

nest. _____ quacked to her ducklings.
            5

_____ followed Mother Duck as _____
     6   7

headed for the pond. One by one the ducklings

followed _____ into the water. _____ all
                  8   9

swam happily together around the pond.

Revise

Each underlined pronoun in the paragraph below is incorrect. Write the correct pronoun above each underlined word.

Do you like tomatoes? Did <u>we</u> know that at one time almost everyone in
          1

the United States thought <u>them</u> were poisonous? People grew tomatoes
                   2

in <u>them</u> gardens only because <u>his</u> fruit was pretty. There is a story that one
   3   4

day a man took some tomatoes to town and offered <u>him</u> to the people
                                            5

who passed by. No one would touch <u>their</u>. So the man ate <u>it</u> all up. <u>She</u>
                             6   7   8

did not die. The news spread. <u>I</u> helped people change <u>them</u> minds about
                          9   10

tomatoes.

Tips for Your Own Writing: Revising ....

When you speak, you can use a lot of pronouns because you can point to
people and things. When you write, make sure your pronouns point to nouns.

*Pronouns make sense when they clearly refer to someone or
something.*

113

Grammar: Verbs

The game is tied. Michael Jordan runs, jumps, shoots, and scores! Bulls win, Bulls win! A verb is the action word in a sentence.

.... Did You Know? ....

A *verb* is a word that shows action or expresses a state of being. Every sentence must have a verb. A verb such as *Go!* can be a one-word sentence.

***Jump, shoot, listen,* and *read* are action verbs.**

***Am, are, is, was, were, be, being,* and *been* are all forms of the verb *be*. They tell what someone or something is, was, or will be.**

A *present tense* verb shows action that happens now.

The farmer **plants** corn in early spring.

A *past tense* verb shows action that happened earlier.

The farmer **planted** beans in that field last year.

A *future tense* verb shows action that will happen.

Next year, the farmer **will plant** barley.

Show What You Know

Underline every verb in the paragraph below. Write *present*, *past*, or *future* above each verb to tell when the action takes place.

There is an ancient Greek legend about a nine-headed dragon that lived in

a lake. The dragon attacked sailing ships. Many people said, "Kill the dragon."

Each time one head was cut off, another head grew in its place. Hercules

knew what to do. He cut off each head and sealed the neck with fire.

Score: _____   Total Possible: 20

Practice

Write a verb in each blank. You can shape the paragraph with the verbs you choose.

A zoo is a fun place to _____. People _____ the way

animals _____. Monkeys _____ up rocks or _____

from tree to tree chasing other monkeys. In the reptile house,

snakes _____ down tree trunks.

Their tongues _____ in and out. The

slow-moving elephants _____ over

to the water in their pen and fill their trunks.

Then they arch their trunks over their

heads and _____ the water all

over their bodies to stay cool.

Revise

Write a more interesting verb above each underlined verb.

Woolly mammoths <u>walked</u> on Earth more than three million years ago.
These creatures <u>were</u> about eleven feet tall. They <u>seemed</u> like hairy elephants.
Mammoths <u>had</u> moss, grass, and twigs. Early humans <u>killed</u> the woolly
mammoth for food and clothing. The last woolly mammoths <u>ended</u> about ten
thousand years ago.

Tips for Your Own Writing: Revising ....

In your own story writing, check that your verbs are in the appropriate tense:
past tense, present tense, or future tense.

 You're really taking some action when you use verbs!

56 Grammar: Adjectives

You've just come home and you're starving. On the kitchen table is a basket filled with crisp red apples, golden-yellow bananas, and juicy ripe peaches. See how adjectives can add flavor to your writing!

...... Did You Know? ......

An *adjective* is a word that describes a noun or pronoun. *Crisp, red, golden-yellow, juicy,* and *ripe* describe the fruit in the sentence above.

Adjectives tell a reader *what kind* and *how many.*

Clouds can be **soft**, **fluffy**, **threatening**, or **black**. Adjectives usually come before the nouns they describe but can come after the verb.

crying baby   **six** balloons   **sour** pickle

An adjective is a word that can fit in both these blanks: The _____ tree is very _____.

The **tall** tree is very **tall**.

Show What You Know

Circle the adjectives in the paragraph below.

On a crisp, cool evening, Donna, a young Alaskan girl, was watching television. A short message flashed across the screen: "Great auroras out tonight." Donna pulled on her warm parka and went outside. Twin pathways of greenish-white light arced across the dark sky. As Donna watched the shining trail, a red border grew along its bottom edge. Suddenly the ball of light exploded, shooting colorful rays in many directions.

Score: _____   Total Possible: 15

Practice

Write an adjective on each blank. Two are shown as examples.

On a vacation, a family played a game called "I Spy." Each person described something he or she saw. Then they repeated what everyone else had seen, but they changed the words that described each thing. Here is their game:

"I spy ____blue____ water."

"I spy a _____ whale and ___choppy___ water."

"I spy a _____ dog, a _____ whale, and _____ water."

"I spy some _____ wildflowers, a _____ dog, a _____ whale, and _____ water."

Revise

Write a more descriptive adjective above each of the underlined adjectives in the following paragraph.

When Sara decided to join the band, she had to choose an instrument to play. Would she pick a <u>big</u> trumpet? How about a <u>loud</u> bass drum? Sara
₁   ₂
always liked the <u>nice</u> sound of the flute. She also liked the <u>low</u>, rumbling
              ₃   ₄
sound of the tuba. There were so many <u>good</u> instruments that it was hard to
                                    ₅
decide. What do you think she chose?

Tips for Your Own Writing: Revising ....

Check a story you have written. Make sure you have placed your adjectives before the nouns or after verbs like *be* and *feel*.

✏️ **G**ifted, stupendous, *and* wonderful—*all are adjectives that describe good work.*

57 Grammar: Adverbs

We went to the beginners' band concert. Some students played well, others played enthusiastically, and a few played badly.

.... Did You Know? ....

Adverbs can describe verbs. They tell *when, where,* or *how* an action happens.

The concert will start **soon.** (*Soon* tells when.)
The tuba player sits **here.** (*Here* tells where.)
The drummer plays **loudly.** (*Loudly* tells how.)

Adverbs can describe adjectives. They usually answer the question *how*.

quite handsome   **too** small   **rather** sweet

My **really** naughty dog chews **very** old slippers.
   How naughty is my dog? *Really* naughty. How
   old are the slippers? *Very* old.

Adverbs can also describe other adverbs.

very quickly   **extremely** slowly   **awfully** quietly

Show What You Know

Circle the adverb that describes the verb in bold type. Then circle the question that the adverb answers.

1. The game **started** early in the afternoon.   How?   When?   Where?

2. The Bombers confidently **took** the field.   How?   When?   Where?

3. The batter **walked** slowly to home plate.   How?   When?   Where?

4. The pitcher **threw** there.   How?   When?   Where?

5. The batter easily **hit** the ball.   How?   When?   Where?

6. The crowd **applauded** loudly.   How?   When?   Where?

Score: _____   Total Possible: 12

Practice

Write adverbs on the blank lines to describe the verbs in each sentence.

Mr. Walsh _____ described the science

1
experiments to the class. Robbie _____

2
volunteered to grow crystals. He filled a jar
with water, and _____ added sugar. He

3
tied a string to a pencil and suspended it in the
water. _____ , he put the jar in the

4
sunlight. Each morning he _____ checked

5
the jar. _____ , a few small specks appeared

6
on the string. Robbie reported _____ that his experiment was working!

7

Revise

Adverbs add details to your writing. Different adverbs can be used to change the meanings of sentences. Replace the underlined adverbs. Write your adverbs above the underlined ones.

Birthday parties are so much fun. Guests come bringing <u>nicely</u> wrapped

1
gifts. During the games, everyone cheers <u>happily</u>. They sing <u>strongly</u> as the

2   3
cake's candles are <u>rapidly</u> lit. The candles shine <u>wonderfully</u>, while everyone

4   5
waits <u>noiselessly</u> for the wish. Later we talk <u>loudly</u> as the gifts are opened

6   7
and each one is lifted <u>slowly</u> out of its box.

8

Tips for Your Own Writing: Revising ....

Look at a report you have written. Would your report be better if you added adverbs that tell when, where, and how?

Surely, you can tell that all adverbs describe verbs, adjectives, or other adverbs well.

58 Grammar: Articles

Little words can make a big difference. Good writers pay attention to all details, big and small.

.... Did You Know? ....

A, *an*, and *the* are useful words called <u>articles</u>. You can think of them as noun signals. They tell the reader there is a noun coming in the sentence.

A and *an* tell about any person, place, thing, or idea. Use *a* with nouns that start with a consonant.

a ball   **a** jump rope   **a** zebra

Use *an* with nouns that start with a vowel sound.

an egg   **an** oyster   **an** umbrella

***The* tells about a specific person, place, thing, or idea.**

Give me **the** apple, please.

Show What You Know

Underline each word in the sentences below that signals any person, place, thing, or idea. Circle each word that signals a specific person, place, thing, or idea.

We took my brother Jim to college last week. I had never been to a big

university before. The campus was as big as a small town. Jim has classes in

several different buildings. We visited a science building and the library. The

dormitory where Jim lives is a ten-story building. The cafeteria and study

rooms are on the first floor. The computer lab is on the fifth floor.

Score: _____   **Total Possible: 11**

Practice

Choose the article that best completes each sentence below. Write the articles in the blanks.

What if you were on _____ deserted
1
island and you wanted fruit to eat? You couldn't
buy it at _____ grocery store. You would have
2
to find it. You will first need to know if _____
3
fruit is safe to eat. _____ red fruit looks safe.
4
What about _____ yellow fruit, _____ white fruit, or _____ bunch of
5   6   7
green ones? Can you pick between _____ green or _____ yellow piece
8   9
of fruit? How about _____ orange fruit? This should be _____ easy
10   11
choice.

Revise

Read each underlined article below. If it is not correct, write the correct article above each underlined one.

<u>A</u> animal's tail can come in handy in many ways. <u>An</u> horse can use its tail
1   2
to chase away <u>an</u> insect. <u>An</u> tail of <u>the</u> fish is used to push it through <u>a</u>
3   4   5   6
water. <u>An</u> monkey hangs by its tail so that its hands are free to find food. <u>An</u>
7   8
beaver smacks its tail on <u>a</u> water when danger is near. <u>A</u> skunk raises its tail
9   10
as <u>the</u> warning that it is about to spray.
11

Tips for Your Own Writing: Revising ....

Check your writing to make sure you have used *a* and *an* correctly. *A* is used
when a word begins with a consonant sound, and *an* is used when a word
begins with a vowel sound.

A *word and* the *word are two very different words, indeed!*

59 Review: Parts of Speech

A. **Read the paragraph below. Underline sixteen nouns.**

Harriet Tubman was born a slave in 1820 in Maryland. She escaped from a plantation in 1849 but had to leave her family behind. Harriet wanted freedom for her people. She helped hide slaves who were on their way to Canada. She was one of the famous conductors on the Underground Railroad. Her bravery helped lead more than 300 people to freedom.

Score: _____   Total Possible: 17

B. **Replace the word or words in bold type with a pronoun. Write the pronoun above the bold word.**

Kay rides home on the six o'clock train. Every day **Kay** meets Bill on
                                                  1
the train. Kay and Bill give the conductor **Kay's and Bill's** tickets, and **the**
                                             2
conductor checks **the tickets.** When the train departs, **the train** is almost
3   4   5
full. The conductor talks to Bill and helps **Bill** put **Bill's** briefcase on the shelf.
                                             6   7

Score: _____   Total Possible: 7

C. **Underline the verb in each sentence. Write a more vivid verb above each one. You can use a verb from the list below.**

| unlocked | walked | escaped | will sleep |
| searched | raced | returned | ate |

The zookeeper went over to the monkey's cage. He opened the door to the cage. The monkeys left. The zookeeper looked everywhere for the monkeys. The monkeys ran through the park. They had hot dogs, peanuts, and popcorn. Then they went back to their cage. The monkeys will rest after their exciting day.

Score: _____   Total Possible: 16

D. Complete each sentence by filling in the five blank spaces with adjectives.

The baby birds waited patiently in their _____ nest. The nest was
1

safe in a _____ tree. Soon the mother bird returned to feed her
2

_____ babies. The mother bird carried a _____ worm in her
3   4

beak. _____ baby birds and only one worm—what should she do?
5

E. Underline the nine adverbs in the paragraph below.

The sky darkened slowly all afternoon. Finally, it began to snow. The flakes

drifted lazily over the grass and trees. The ground was soon covered with a

soft, white blanket. The wind suddenly shifted, and the storm quickly began.

The wind roared loudly through the tree branches. The snow swiftly piled

against the windows. Within an hour, it was at least a foot deep.

**F. Choose the article (*a, an, the*) that best completes each sentence.
Write it on the line.**

"To live long, live hidden" is the motto of many animals. For some

animals, _____ best defense is to hold completely still so that their predators
1

won't notice them. Some animals are protected by _____ change in color
2

that can make them almost invisible. In polar areas, _____ creature might
3

have fur that turns white to blend in with _____ snow. Spots and stripes can
4

help other animals hide in _____ area with tall grass or leaves.
5

60 Grammar: Statements and Questions I

Do you know that there are different kinds of sentences? A good writer knows exactly when to use each kind.

Did You Know?

A sentence can be a statement or a question.

A __statement__ is a sentence that gives information. It ends with a period (.).

Dalmatians are large dogs with black spots**.**
They do not have spots when they are born**.**

A __question__ is a sentence that asks for information. It ends with a question mark (?).

How are dalmatian puppies different from adults**?**
What do dalmatians look like**?**

Show What You Know

Add a period or a question mark to each of the sentences in the paragraph.

What scared the impala It was a leopard that leaped out of the bush

Leopards hunt other animals by sneaking up on them They eat reptiles and

small mammals Leopards do not have very many enemies Baboons, lions, and

hyenas will attack baby leopards Who is the leopard's greatest enemy It is the

people who hunt leopards for their beautiful coats

Score: _____   Total Possible: 8

Practice

Write two sentences that give information.

1._____

_____

2._____

_____

_____

Revise

**Now, try making questions out of the statements you wrote above.
You can use words like *who*, *what*, *where*, *when*, *why*, or *how* to make
questions.**

1._____

_____

2._____

_____

Tips for Your Own Writing: Revising ....

When you are checking your writing, look for sentences that begin with such
words as *who*, *what*, *where*, *when*, *why*, and *how*. These words often begin
questions. Be sure you placed a question mark at the end of sentences that
begin with these words and ask a question.

*In sentences that ask, use a question mark; in sentences that tell,
use a period.*

61 Grammar: Statements and Questions II

Statements tell and questions ask.

·························· **Did You Know?** ··························

Some sentences tell facts and others ask questions. Each kind of sentence has its own job to do. Each kind of sentence uses a different end mark.

A sentence that gives information is a statement and ends with a period.

> Most deserts get less than ten inches of rain in a year.

A sentence that asks for information is a question and ends with a question mark.

> How much rain do most deserts get in a year?

···

Show What You Know

Add a period to each sentence that is a statement. Add a question mark to the end of each sentence that asks for information.

Where do the President and his family live The President's home is at

1600 Pennsylvania Avenue Have you ever heard of the White House Gang

They were the six children of President Theodore Roosevelt They had lots of

fun when they lived in the White House They roller-skated in the halls, slid

down the steps on trays, and walked on stilts in the flower gardens They had

many pets—dogs, cats, rabbits, birds, and a pony Once they brought their

pony upstairs in an elevator What do you think President Roosevelt said when

the elevator door opened Who would have believed there was a pony on the

elevator

Score: _____   **Total Possible: 10**

Practice

Your home is not as famous as the White House, but there are probably lots of interesting facts about it. Make a list of facts about your home.

_____

_____

_____

_____

_____

_____

Revise

Now, pretend that you are giving a friend a tour of your home. Write a conversation that you and your friend might have. Use your list of facts to write questions and statements.

_____

_____

_____

_____

Tips for Your Own Writing: Revising ....

Choose a piece of your own writing. Underline sentences that ask for information. Check to make sure that each underlined sentence ends with a question mark.

Ask me a question, and I will answer in a statement.

62 Grammar: Exclamations

In writing, to say it with feeling, use an exclamation point.

.... **Did You Know?** ....

A sentence that expresses strong feeling is an <u>exclamatory</u> sentence. It ends with an exclamation point.

It was so hot**!**
Look at the beautiful sunset**!**
Be careful**!**

When you are reading, end punctuation marks tell you what tone of voice you would use if you were speaking. In this way, periods, question marks, and exclamation points are signposts for the reader.

Read the sentences aloud. Notice how your voice changes as you read each one.

I'm hungry!
Where are we going?
Nick ate cereal and fruit for breakfast.

• •

Show What You Know

After each sentence, add the correct punctuation.

A little green man was sitting at the table when I got home from school

He said that his name was Zornak and that he came from outer space He had

eaten all the food in the kitchen Boy, Mom's going to be mad about that I

heard steps on the porch Where should I hide him "Hurry, get in the closet"

My little brother Eddie came into the room Could I trust him with my secret

Here goes nothing I opened the closet door "Eddie, meet Zornak," I said

Score: _____   **Total Possible: 12**

128

Practice

Pretend you came home from school and found something unexpected in your house. Write a paragraph that tells about what you found and how you reacted.

_____

_____

_____

_____

_____

_____

_____

Revise

Review your paragraph. Rewrite two sentences to show strong feelings. Be sure to end those sentences with exclamation points.

_____

_____

_____

_____

Tips for Your Own Writing: Revising ....

You use an exclamation point at the end of a sentence to show strong feelings. Using too many exclamation points weakens their meaning. Not everything is exciting. Check your writing. If you have used more than two or three exclamation points, you may want to change some of them to periods.

When feelings are strong, exclamation points belong!

63 Grammar: Statements, Questions, and Exclamations

✏️ *"Have I used the correct punctuation?" is an important question to ask.*

Did You Know?

Writers use different kinds of sentences.

Most sentences will be statements.

Uncle Jon likes to barbecue.

Some will ask questions.

Does he cook outside often?

A few sentences will express strong feelings, like excitement, anger, surprise, or fear. This kind of sentence ends with an exclamation point (!).

His smoked chicken is out-of-this-world!

Show What You Know

Add correct punctuation to the end of each sentence in the paragraph.

It is a hot, sunny day in southern Florida Do you see an area of swirling clouds off the coast Wind speeds are more than 100 miles per hour Weather reporters name this storm Hurricane Barbara The storm is strong enough to rip trees out of the ground The giant, spinning mass of clouds gains speed over the water The winds shape the clouds into an enormous doughnut Will it move west to the coast, or will it head out to sea Sometimes computers can predict the path of a storm Other times, the hurricane has a mind of its own

Score: _____   Total Possible: 10

Practice

Choose one of the questions from the list below. Write two statements that answer the question.

Should my school require students to wear uniforms?

Is a cat a better pet than a dog?

Do you like the Fourth of July? Why or why not?

1._____

_____

2._____

_____

Revise

Review the sentences you have written. Now change your statements into questions but not the same questions as those given above. Make sure you use question marks at the end of your questions.

1._____

_____

2._____

_____

Tips for Your Own Writing: Revising ....

Most of the sentences you write will be statements. Check to make sure they end with periods. When you do ask questions, always end the sentences with question marks. To show strong feelings, you can end your sentences with an exclamation point.

When a sentence tells, a period is swell. For a question, it's true that a question mark will do.

64 Review: Sentence Types

A. **Use proper proofreading marks to add a period or question mark at the end of each of the ten sentences.**

Koalas are small, furry animals that live in Australia Why did the aborigines call these mammals koalas *Koala* means "one who doesn't drink" How do koalas get the water they need They eat tender eucalyptus leaves that are almost two-thirds water No other animal in the forest eats eucalyptus The koalas spend most of their lives high in the eucalyptus trees Do they ever come down They come down to move to another tree to find more food A koala eats about two pounds of leaves a day

Score: _____   **Total Possible: 10**

B. **Here is part of a story. The writer forgot to use end marks. Use proper proofreading marks to add periods and question marks to twelve sentences.**

We have been in the desert for two days The midday sun shimmers on the hot sand We are almost out of water Are my eyes playing tricks on me Sometimes people think they see water in the desert Right over the next dune, I see a cool, blue pool of water surrounded by lush, green trees Is that a camel Is he sitting on a lawn chair sipping a glass of lemonade I run toward the oasis I feel someone tapping on my arm I wake up from my nap at the pool and see my sister She says, "How about a nice, cool drink"

Score: _____   **Total Possible: 12**

C. Only periods were used in this paragraph. Use proofreading marks to revise three sentences by changing one period to a question mark and two periods to exclamation points.

Imagine living in the age of the dinosaurs. What do you think you would see. The area around you would be filled with unfamiliar plants and trees. You would see some peaceful, plant-eating animals. You might run into some fierce, flesh-eating killers, too. A brachiosaurus was as long as three school buses and as tall as a five-story building. It could have weighed as much as sixteen elephants. Others were as small as a chicken. Ornithopods were little, but they could sprint as fast as a galloping horse.

Score: _____   **Total Possible: 3**

D. Choose one group of words from Column A and one from Column B to make sentences. Make two statements, one question, and one exclamatory sentence using the correct end marks.

Column A	Column B
We live in a galaxy	a shooting star
How many	around 500,000 million stars in our galaxy
There are	called the Milky Way
Look! I see	stars are in our galaxy

_____

_____

_____

Score: _____   **Total Possible: 4**

REVIEW SCORE: _____   **REVIEW TOTAL: 29**

65 Grammar: Understanding Sentences I

*W*riting a sentence is easy if you tell who or what did what.

.... **Did You Know?** ....

A *sentence* tells *who* or *what*, and it tells *what happens*.

> **My dog Buster won first prize.**
> (tells who)   (tells what happened)

Show What You Know

Underline the groups of words that are sentences.

1. Hannibal lives in a cage.

2. A small, chunky hamster.

3. He has a short tail and chubby cheeks.

4. His fur is reddish-brown.

5. The pouches in his cheeks.

6. Sleeps all day.

7. Fruit, grains, and raw vegetables make up Hannibal's diet.

8. He runs on a little wheel.

9. In his cage.

10. Lots of fun.

Score: _____   **Total Possible: 5**

Practice

Make the sentences below complete. For some sentences, you must add words that tell who or what. For other sentences, you must add words that tell what happened.

1. The girls _____.

2. _____ lived near Boulder, Colorado.

3. Her house _____.

4. _____ wears glasses.

Revise

Read the paragraph. Underline the three incomplete sentences. Add words that tell who, what, or what happened and write the corrected sentences on the lines.

    Our apartment has only two bedrooms. <u>My two little brothers and I.</u> John and Matt are lucky. <u>Get to sleep in bunk beds.</u> I sleep in a bed on the other side of the room. Sometimes, I wish I had my own room. <u>Then my friends and I.</u> Sometimes, I like sharing a room. We all have to clean it even when only I made the mess.

_____

_____

_____

Tips for Your Own Writing: Revising ....

When checking a sentence you have written, ask yourself: Does my sentence tell who, what, or what happened? If your answer is *no,* then you must revise your sentence until you can answer *yes.*

 ***A** sentence won't work if it's missing parts!*

66 Grammar: Understanding Sentences II

Reading short, choppy sentences can be boring. Once you get your readers started, help them keep rolling. Sometimes putting sentences together can make your writing flow more smoothly.

······························· **Did You Know?** ·····························

Sometimes two sentences have ideas that are equally important. They can be joined to make one sentence using a comma and the word and.

> Springfield is the capital of Illinois.
> Madison is the capital of Wisconsin.
> Springfield is the capital of Illinois, **and** Madison is the capital of Wisconsin.

If the ideas in two sentences seem opposed to each other, use a comma and the word but to join them.

> My dog is really ugly.   I love him anyway.
> My dog is really ugly, **but** I love him anyway.

If there is a choice in the two sentences, use a comma and the word or to join them.

> We can visit the aquarium. We can go to the zoo instead.
> We can visit the aquarium, **or** we can go to the zoo instead.

Show What You Know

Choose *and*, *or*, or *but* to join each set of sentences. Write the new sentences. Do not forget to add a comma before *and*, *but*, or *or*.

Mary is my older sister. Megan is my younger sister.

1._____

We get along pretty well. Sometimes we fight over using the telephone.

2._____

Score: _____   Total Possible: 2

Practice

Look at the picture. Write two sentences to describe what is happening using *and*, *or*, or *but*.

_____

_____

_____

_____

Revise

Read the following paragraph. Use proofreading marks to add *and*, *but*, or *or* to combine four sentences that you think should go together. Remember to place a comma before *and*, *but*, or *or*.

Example: I like to collect baseball cards. My sister doesn't.
                                                    but

   Do you like to collect sports cards? My sister and I do. I collect baseball cards. My sister collects basketball cards. I keep my cards in a shoe box. My sister organizes all her cards in a photo album. My older brother used to collect baseball cards, too. He doesn't anymore. Maybe he will give his cards to me. Maybe he will sell them. I hope he gives them to me.

Tips for Your Own Writing: Revising ....

Sometimes you may write short sentences that can be combined. Check that you place a comma before the *and*, *but*, or *or* when you combine them. Make sure you use *and* to connect sentences with similar ideas, use *but* to connect sentences with opposing ideas, and use *or* to connect sentences that give choices.

If combining sentences is what you want to do, a comma and and, but, *or* or *can always help you.*

67 Grammar: Combining Sentences I

✏️ *When two people or things do the same thing, try to tell about it in one sentence when you can!*

.... Did You Know? ....

To combine sentences that have some of the words repeated, use the repeated words only once and the word and to join the sentences. Remember to change the verb form to agree with the plural subject.

> Maria likes to hike in the mountains.
> Tanya likes to hike in the mountains.
> **Maria and Tanya like** to hike in the mountains.

If you use I as part of a combined subject, do not forget to put I last.

> **I** am going to summer camp.
> **Keith** is going to summer camp.
> **Keith and I** are going to summer camp.

Show What You Know

Combine each set of sentences below to form one sentence. Use *and* to connect two nouns or pronouns.

1. My grandpa collects stamps. I collect stamps.

_____

2. My sister sometimes gives me stamps. My dad sometimes gives me stamps.

_____

3. Rare stamps are valuable. Stamps with printing errors are valuable.

_____

Score: _____   **Total Possible: 3**

Practice

On another piece of paper, make a Venn diagram to show how one of your hobbies and a classmate's hobby are the same.

My Hobby   Classmate's Hobby

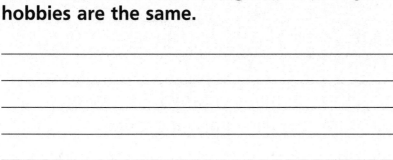

model airplane
my father started
my collection

Both
are
collections.

model car
my grandma started
my collection

Write two sentences telling about how your hobbies are the same.

_____

_____

_____

_____

Revise

Rewrite each pair of sentences below to form one sentence.

1. Peas never stay on your fork. Meatballs never stay on your fork.

_____

2. Lemons will make you pucker. Sour grapes will make you pucker.

_____

Tips for Your Own Writing: Revising ....

Remember that you must change the verb to agree with a combined subject. Also be sure to place the pronoun *I* last if you combine it with another pronoun or a noun as part of a subject.

To combine subjects, the rules are these: subject and verb must agree, and I goes last in order to please.

68 Grammar: Combining Sentences II

If you have one person doing more than one thing, then place the verbs in a string.

.... Did You Know? ....

A good writer can combine sentences in several ways. One way is to combine two sentences that have some of the words repeated. Use the repeated words only once, and use *and* or *or* to join the sentences.

Gloria washed the dishes. Gloria dried the dishes.
Gloria washed **and** dried the dishes.

Gloria dusted the furniture. Gloria vacuumed the carpet.
Gloria dusted the furniture **and** vacuumed the carpet.

Show What You Know

Combine each pair of sentences below into one sentence that has two verbs, or action words.

1. Helen Keller could not see. Helen Keller could not hear.

_____

2. Helen could read Braille. Helen could write on a special typewriter.

_____

3. She went to high school. She graduated from Radcliffe College.

_____

4. Helen wrote books. Helen received many honors for helping others.

_____

Score: _____   Total Possible: 4

Practice

Think about a person who interests you. Write down action words that you might use to tell about the person (wrote, published, invented). Then write two short sentences with compound action verbs about the person.

_____

_____

_____

_____

Revise

Combine each pair of sentences below by using repeated words only once. Use the word _and_ to connect the verbs and their objects in the sentences.

1. Frédéric Bartholdi, from France, built a giant metal statue. Frédéric Bartholdi called it the Statue of Liberty.

_____

_____

2. The statue was built so that people can climb up inside. People look out through the crown.

_____

Tips for Your Own Writing: Revising ....

Find a piece of your own writing. Look for two sentences that tell about the same person, place, thing, or idea. If you find any, combine them into one.

_O_ne subject and two verbs can be combined to make your sentences more refined.

69 Grammar: Combining Sentences III

If readers you want to win, avoid writing sentences that repeat the same words again and again.

.... **Did You Know?** ....

A good writer can combine sentences in several ways. One way is to use *and* to combine sentences that have some of the words repeated so that the repeated words are used only once.

> Kenji likes apples. Kenji likes oranges.
> Kenji likes apples **and** oranges.

If more than two things are named, put a comma after each one, and add *and* before the last one.

> Veronica has a dog. Veronica has a cat. Veronica has two goldfish.
> Veronica has a dog**,** a cat**, and** two goldfish.

Show What You Know

Combine each set of sentences below into one sentence.

1. Our class took a trip to New York City. Our class took a trip to Washington, D.C.

   _____

2. We traveled by plane. We traveled by train. We traveled by bus.

   _____

3. We saw the Empire State Building. We saw the World Trade Center. We saw the Washington Monument.

   _____

Score: _____   Total Possible: 3

Practice

Look at the picture. Write two sentences with compound parts to describe what you see. Keep your sentences short and to the point.

1._____

 _____

 _____

2._____

 _____

Revise

Combine the following sets of sentences to avoid repeating words.

1. Elephants eat leaves. Elephants eat grass and fruit.

 _____

2. The African elephant has four toenails on its front feet. The African elephant has three toenails on its back feet.

 _____

3. Today, many African and Asian countries protect the elephants. Today many African and Asian nations protect their habitats.

 _____

Tips for Your Own Writing: Revising ....

When you combine more than two items in a sentence, make sure you place a comma after each item except the last one. Write the word *and* before the last item listed.

One subject and one verb can stand with many words when you use and.

143

70 Grammar: Combining Sentences IV

Sometimes one sentence will do in place of two.

.... Did You Know? ....

Sometimes you can improve your writing by using one or two words in place of a whole sentence.

Grandma baked muffins. They were delicious.
Grandma baked **delicious** muffins.

You can often combine basic information from several sentences into one sentence.

Grandma has a garden. It is in the backyard. It is big.
Grandma has a **big** garden **in the backyard** *or*
Grandma has a **big, backyard** garden.

Show What You Know

Combine each group of sentences below into one sentence.

1. Rosa is going on a trip. She is going to Dallas. The trip is short.

_____

2. She packs a suitcase. It is brown. It is big.

_____

3. Uncle Larry carries the suitcase to the car. The suitcase is heavy.

_____

4. Doug meets Rosa at the airport. Rosa is Doug's cousin.

_____

Score: _____   **Total Possible: 4**

Practice

Look at the picture and write two sentences with two adjectives connected by *and* to tell what the lucky pirate found.

1. _____

   _____

   _____

2. _____

   _____

Revise

Combine the following pairs of sentences. Write your sentences on the lines.

1. A sheepdog has long hair. Its shaggy hair covers its eyes.

   _____

2. A dachshund's legs are short. Its stumpy legs are powerful.

   _____

3. The Chihuahua has bulging eyes. The eyes are very large.

   _____

Tips for Your Own Writing: Revising ....

When you are proofreading sentences you have combined, make sure that you have not added adjectives that have the same or similar meanings.

When possible, replace a sentence with a word or two to make your writing more efficient.

71 Grammar: Combining Sentences V

✏ *Using phrases in sentences lets you say more—with less!*

·························· ## Did You Know? ·······················

In writing, you can combine short sentences to save space and add variety. Sometimes you can improve your writing by using a phrase in place of a whole sentence.

> My birthday present was a CD player. It was from Mom and Dad.

> My birthday present **from Mom and Dad** was a CD player.

Show What You Know

Combine each pair of sentences into one sentence. Use a phrase in place of one sentence.

1. Oscar went sailing. He went with Ramon.

_____

2. They sailed east. They left from the harbor.

_____

3. Oscar had supplies. He stored them beneath the deck.

_____

4. They docked the boat. The dock was past the cove.

_____

5. Oscar and Ramon had a picnic. They sat near some rocks.

_____

Score: _____   **Total Possible: 5**

Practice

Write a poem by adding nouns, verbs, and other words to the following phrases.

_____ in the house.

_____ by a mouse.

_____ across the floor.

_____ out the door.

Revise

In the paragraph below, combine sentences by using phrases. Write your new sentences on the lines.

Mars is the fourth planet from the sun. Mars is in our solar system. Mars looks red because iron oxide is in the soil. Iron oxide is also in the rocks. Mars is the only planet besides Earth with ice caps. The ice caps are located at the poles.

_____

_____

_____

_____

_____

Tips for Your Own Writing: Revising ....

You can use words like *above, across, before, during, from, in, into, on, over, under,* and *with* to begin a phrase when revising your writing.

"During the nights and the days" is an example of a phrase.

72 Review: Sentences

A. Add the missing words to complete each of the seven sentences.

The animals who live in Animalville lead a different life than most other animals. In the morning, they _____1___. _____2_____ have a picnic lunch. Sometimes the baby monkeys _____3___. _____4_____ the trees with balloons and streamers. The baby tigers _____5_____. _____6_____ make the other animals laugh. All the animals _____7_____.

Score: _____   **Total Possible: 7**

B. Combine each pair of sentences below into one compound sentence. You may want to use *and*, *but*, or *or* to connect the sentences.

1. Brian and Karen went to the video store. They looked for a movie.

_____

2. Karen wanted to rent *Babe*. Brian had already seen it.

_____

3. Brian decided to get *The Indian in the Cupboard*. Karen liked his choice.

_____

4. They have to return the movie tomorrow. The video store will charge a $2 late fee.

_____

Score: _____   **Total Possible: 4**

C. Combine the following sentences by making the subjects, verbs, or objects compound.

1. Hidori helped Dad plan a trip. Lee helped Dad plan a trip.

_____

2. In the car, Hidori read. Hidori listened to the radio.

_____

3. They visited a zoo. They visited a planetarium. They visited a museum.

_____

Score: _____   Total Possible: 3

D. Combine each set of sentences into one sentence.

1. Kangaroos are furry mammals. They are unusual.

_____

2. Kangaroos hop on their powerful hind legs. Their legs are long.

_____

Score: _____   Total Possible: 2

E. Combine each pair of sentences into one sentence. Use a phrase in place of a sentence.

1. Bears are big and powerful animals. They are animals with long, thick fur.

_____

2. Bear cubs live with their mother. They stay with her for about one or two years.

_____

Score: _____   Total Possible: 2

REVIEW SCORE: _____   REVIEW TOTAL: 18

149

Writer's Handbook

Getting Started with the Writing Process

 Writing is a picture of words.

······················· **Did You Know?** ·······························

Writing is like drawing a picture. Follow the steps of the writing process, and you will write a good description.

1. **Select** a topic you know. Look around you for ideas. Draw or write about whatever you see. Let's say you decide to write about your home. Write *home* on your paper and circle it. Draw smaller circles around the bigger one.

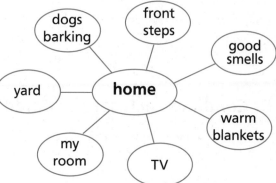

2. **Collect** your ideas by closing your eyes and thinking about your home. Write the words you think of in the smaller circles. Don't worry about spelling.

3. **Connect** or group the words in the small circles that go together or tell about the same thing.

4. **Draft** the words you connected by putting them into sentences. Try to describe your home so that someone who reads your description can see it clearly in his or her mind.

5. **Revise,** or change, anything that doesn't fit when you read the description aloud. Ask a friend to help you find mistakes.

6. **Proofread** your final copy aloud. If you find any mistakes, correct them.

Tips for Your Own Writing: ································

- **Select** a topic that you like and **collect** your ideas.
- **Connect** your ideas that tell about the same thing.
- **Draft** your ideas into sentences.
- **Revise** by making changes and fixing mistakes.
- **Proofread** your paper aloud.

 You can "draw" a picture with words.

Writer's Handbook
Getting Ideas

Look, listen, read, draw, and imagine! That's the way to find an idea for your writing!

.... Did You Know? ....

You can get writing ideas from looking, listening, reading, drawing, or imagining. When you are playing, it is easy to decide what to play. Why? You look around and play with whatever you have. You use your imagination.

Your writing ideas come the same way. Look around. Write about what you know or like. Make a list. Circle what you like the most.

For example, try writing the names of three people, things, or animals you know about. Circle the one you know or like the best. The circled word will be the main idea of your piece of writing. Draw five or more lines with smaller circles at the end of them. Next, write something that tells about or describes the word you circled. Does your paper look anything like this?

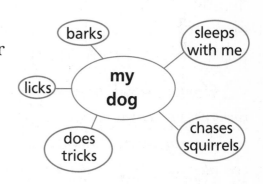

Now you have enough ideas to write a piece. Tell what your writing is about by stating the main idea in the beginning sentence. Then, just write about each idea in the smaller circles. As you write, add ideas as they come to mind.

Tips for Your Own Writing: ....

• Make a list of things that interest you.
• Circle the one that you know about the most.
• Draw circles for five words or phrases that tell about the main idea.
• Write your piece putting your main idea in the first sentence.

Look around you! Write about what you know or would like to know.

Writer's Handbook

Writing a Paragraph

Writing a paragraph can be as easy as A, B, C!

···················· **Did You Know?** ····················

A paragraph has one main idea. All the sentences in a paragraph tell about or give clear details about the main idea. They are also organized in a proper order. Read the following paragraph about an airplane ride.

Courtney and I took our first plane ride. We sat in our seats and fastened our seat belts. We thought our airplane ride was exciting.

The sentences are all in the proper order; however, by adding more details you can make it more interesting. Imagine what you might hear and do on an airplane ride. Read the following paragraph to see how more details can make a paragraph more interesting.

Courtney and I nervously prepared for our very first plane ride. The engines were revving up as we sat down and fastened our seat belts. The plane began backing up, and soon we were zooming down the runway. Up in the air and over the clouds we flew. Our ears plugged up and it was hard to hear. All too soon, our ride was over. We thought our ride was about the most exciting thing we'd ever done.

Which paragraph is more interesting? Which one gives you a clearer picture of what the writer was experiencing? The second one, of course! When you write, try to "show," not "tell," your story.

Tips for Your Own Writing: ······································

- Make sure each sentence in your paragraph tells about or gives clear details about the main idea.
- Check to make sure that your paragraph "shows" the reader what you are trying to say.

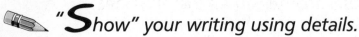

"Show" your writing using details.

Writer's Handbook
Proofreading Checklist

Proofreading takes a sharp eye!

Did You Know?

Did you ever say to yourself, "I didn't write that!" as you read your paper aloud? Sometimes we don't write what we **think** we are writing. This is why we **proofread,** or check, as part of the writing process.

Here are some things to check for:

1. Read your paper aloud and look for missing or extra words.

2. See if all proper nouns and beginnings of sentences are capitalized.

3. Check for misspelled words.

4. See that each sentence ends with the proper punctuation.

Have you ever been asked to help find something for someone, and you find it right away? In proofreading, you ask a classmate to help you find errors you didn't see yourself.

After you have checked your paper for correct spelling, capital letters, and punctuation, it is time to prepare a neat, final draft and proofread it.

See how the proofreading marks from the inside back cover of this book were used to mark the mistakes in the following paragraph.

Last night a small noise woke ^{me} up. i quickly sat up in bed. My heart was pounding! What could that be? then I heard another sound. "Meow!" said a little voice. It was just ^{my} cat!

Tips for Your Own Writing:

• Read your paper aloud and look for one type of mistake at a time.
• Check for missing words and to see if each sentence makes sense.
• Check for capital letters.
• Check for correct spelling and punctuation.

Proofreading helps you make sure you write what you wanted to write!

Writer's Handbook

5 Description in Stories

*A*dding descriptive words can make your writing more interesting.

······························ **Did You Know?** ·····························

When we tell a story, we use a lot of **vivid** words to make the story seem more real. Words like *soft, bubbly, long, smooth, brown, short, sad,* and *quiet* are some of the words we can use to describe a person, place, or thing. When we use descriptive words, we end up with a much better story.

Below are two ways to describe a room. The words in bold italics are description words. Which set of sentences gives you a better picture?

1. Jonathan has his own room. He likes the way it looks. He picked out his posters.

2. Jonathan has his own room. He likes its *light green* walls and *white* door. It is *small* but *cozy.* On his windows he has *green plaid* curtains. There is a *dark green, furry* rug near his bed. He has a *large, brown* desk. There are *bright* posters of zoo animals on the walls. The posters are Jonathan's favorite part because he picked them out himself.

The use of "sense" words can help the reader better experience your story. Sense words you can use in your stories are:

See: *sparkling, spotted, streaked, foggy, green, shining*

Hear: *dripping, sloshing, shrieking, murmuring, crunching*

Smell: *bread baking, vanilla, clean hair, cut grass, gym locker*

Taste: *sour, sugary, lemony, creamy, peppery, sweet*

Touch: *prickly, silky, bumpy, bristly, furry, icy, fuzzy, slick*

Tips for Your Own Writing: ······························

• Use description to help your reader experience your story.
• Use "sense" words to help you with the description in your story.

*A*n absolutely delightful story will tickle your eardrums!

Writer's Handbook
6 Expository Writing–Writing a Report

What interests you? Write a report about it! Share what you know.

Did You Know?

Here are the five main steps for writing a good report:

1. Once you have chosen an interesting topic, you can make a **K-W-L** chart.

K	W	L
What I Know	What I Want to Know	What I Have Learned

List all the things you know about your topic under **K.** Then, under **W,** list all the questions you have about your topic.

2. Your next step is to gather information at the library. As you read, list the most important things you learn about your topic under the **L** on your chart. Then look at your list of questions again. If there are some you have not found answers to, read some more and add notes under **L.** Put your facts in order. This will help you organize your ideas.

3. Next, decide which items under **K** and **L** go together.

4. Now you are ready to write your report. Write all the important information you remember. After you finish, read your report. Change anything that is in the wrong order or doesn't make sense.

5. Check your work for mistakes in spelling, punctuation, and capital letters. Now write your final copy.

Tips for Your Own Writing:

• Choose a topic you like.
• Make a **K-W-L** chart.
• Read as much as you can about your topic and take notes.
• Use your notes and what you knew before to write about your topic.
• Read your report aloud to yourself and make necessary changes.
• Check your report for mistakes in spelling, punctuation, and capitalization.
• Share your report with another student.

*When you write a report, you **and** your readers learn new things.*

Writer's Handbook

Persuasive Writing

 My point is . . .

.... Did You Know? ....

When you try to talk your parents into letting you stay up later, you are trying to *persuade* them. You want them to **believe** that it is OK. You also want them to **take action** by letting you stay up later.

When planning a persuasive writing, you should first think of all the reasons you have to get the reader to believe or to do what you, the writer, want him or her to do. You can write these reasons in the form of a letter to the person you are trying to convince. Include an introduction that states what you believe or want. Form a conclusion based on your reasons.

Suppose you are trying to convince your mother that you want in-line skates. Write her a letter telling her why you think you need and deserve in-line skates. What can you say that will convince her that you should have them? Also, think of why your mother wouldn't want you to have them, and write reasons to convince her otherwise. For instance, if she said that she can't afford them, tell her you will get a job like cleaning yards to earn the money so that you can buy them yourself. You can also give reasons why the in-line skates would be helpful to you and to your family. If you know of any facts or information that would help to convince her, include those in your letter. Every reason or example you give should support your desire to have in-line skates.

Now put all of your reasons together in a way that makes sense. Revise and edit as many times as necessary. Proofread your final copy.

Tips for Your Own Writing:............................

- Think about what you would like.
- Gather and organize your reasons.
- Write an introduction.
- State your reasons.
- Write a conclusion based on your reasons.

With sound reason, you may find a way to get something you have always wanted.

Writer's Handbook

8 Writing a Friendly Letter

Write a letter and you might receive one!

Did You Know?

Isn't it fun to get a letter in the mail? It makes you feel good. If you want to get a letter, you need to write one. The type of letter you might send to a friend or relative is called a **friendly letter.** You should have a purpose in mind when you write the letter. Maybe you would like to tell your grandparents about an exciting softball game you played in or tell a faraway friend what you have been doing since he or she moved.

Another type of letter you might write is a **thank-you letter.** It should tell what the thank-you letter is for. The following is an example of a thank-you letter:

> 128 Short Street
> Huntington, WV 25703
> January 20, 1997
>
> Dear Aunt Patty,
>
>   Thank you for sending me five dollars for my birthday. I used it to go to a movie and buy pop. I really liked the movie.
>
>   Love,
>   *Kaleigh*

No matter what your reason for writing a letter, it should be clearly written and include all the necessary parts: your address, the date, to whom you are writing, the body, a closing, and a signature. (See page 16.) If you are writing a return letter, answer each question that was asked of you.

Tips for Your Own Writing:

• Does your letter have all the necessary parts?
• Does the body of the letter give all the necessary information?
• Does your letter have the correct punctuation and capitalization?

Receiving letters makes a person feel special. Writing letters makes the writer feel connected to others.

9 An Invitation and an Envelope

An invitation needs to tell what, who, when, and where.

Did You Know?

An invitation can be written in letter form or on cards made especially to be used for invitations. If you are writing an invitation in a letter form, you have to be very careful to include all the necessary information. Those receiving invitations need to know the purpose first. For example, if you are inviting friends to a birthday party, they would need to know that because they would probably want to bring a gift.

Next, you need to let the people know when the activity is taking place. You not only need to tell them the date, but also the day and time. If you want a definite ending time, be sure to include that, also.

Then, add where the activity is taking place. For example, if it is being held outside, people need to dress according to the weather.

If the party is held for someone in particular, such as a birthday party, be sure to give the person's name. Otherwise, just give your name.

Lastly, decide if you want people to let you know whether or not they are coming. Be sure to include the initials R.S.V.P. and your telephone number if you decide you want to know.

When you mail your invitation, the envelope will look like this:

Anita Sang
328 Lagoon St.
Lakeland, FL 32055 } ⟵ *your name and address*

person written to ⟶ Amanda Yin
her address ⟶ { 254 North Lincoln Street
Lakeland, FL 32056

Tips for Your Own Writing:

- Make sure your invitation includes all the necessary information.
- Don't forget to include your address on the envelope.

Invitations usually cover only one subject!

Writer's Handbook

Word Lists

IRREGULAR VERBS: Below is a partial list of some common irregular verbs.

PRESENT Today I...	PAST Yesterday I...	PAST PARTICIPLE I have...
am	was	been
begin	began	begun
break	broke	broken
come	came	come
do	did	done
draw	drew	drawn
eat	ate	eaten
give	gave	given
go	went	gone
grow	grew	grown
make	made	made
ride	rode	ridden
run	ran	run
say	said	said
see	saw	seen
sing	sang	sung
sit	sat	sat
take	took	taken
think	thought	thought
wear	wore	worn
write	wrote	written

ADJECTIVES: Below are some adjectives that describe what we experience with our senses.

See	Hear	Smell	Taste	Touch
colorful	crunching	burnt	creamy	bristly
foggy	crying	delicious	peppery	fluffy
red	growling	flowery	sour	prickly
short	laughing	smoky	spicy	silky
six	loving	stinky	sugary	smooth
spotted	purring	sweet	sweet	soft

ADVERBS: Below is a partial list of adverbs that tell how, when, and where.

How	When	Where
loudly	early	back
slowly	finally	behind
too	soon	here
very	suddenly	there

159

Postal State and Possession Abbreviations

Use these abbreviations on envelopes to be read by postal workers. In other writing, spell out the names of the states.

States

Alabama	AL
Alaska	AK
Arizona	AZ
Arkansas	AR
California	CA
Colorado	CO
Connecticut	CT
Delaware	DE
Florida	FL
Georgia	GA
Hawaii	HI
Idaho	ID
Illinois	IL
Indiana	IN
Iowa	IA
Kansas	KS
Kentucky	KY
Louisiana	LA
Maine	ME
Maryland	MD
Massachusetts	MA
Michigan	MI
Minnesota	MN
Mississippi	MS
Missouri	MO
Montana	MT
Nebraska	NE
Nevada	NV
New Hampshire	NH
New Jersey	NJ
New Mexico	NM
New York	NY
North Carolina	NC
North Dakota	ND
Ohio	OH
Oklahoma	OK
Oregon	OR
Pennsylvania	PA
Rhode Island	RI
South Carolina	SC
South Dakota	SD
Tennessee	TN
Texas	TX
Utah	UT
Vermont	VT
Virginia	VA
Washington	WA
West Virginia	WV
Wisconsin	WI
Wyoming	WY
District of Columbia	DC

U.S. Possessions

American Samoa	AS
Guam	GU
Puerto Rico	PR
Virgin Islands	VI